Radio Nature

by
Renato Romero

*The reception and study
of naturally originating radio
signals*

Published by the Radio Society of Great Britain, 3 Abbey Court, Priory Business Park, Bedford, MK44 3WH. Tel 01234 832 700 Web www.rsgb.org

First published 2008
Reprinted 2008 & 2009
Digitally Reprinted 2010 onwards

Cover design: Dorotea Vizer, M3VZR

Production: Mark Allgar, M1MPA

English version editing: Alan Melia, G3NYK, Mike Dennison, G3XDV

Digitally printed in Great Britain by Page Bros of Norwich

ISBN 9781-9050-8638-2

This book is dedicated to the memory
of the late Ezio Mognaschi, 1940-2006:
Friend, research partner, and professor
of Physics at Pavia University, Italy

Warning!

Elevated metal objects (such as antennas) may attract lightning strikes during a storm. The effects of a direct or even a secondary strike can be fatal. Even ground probes (and Earth dipoles) can attract a strike. Benjamin Franklin was a very lucky man! Even without a direct strike, induced potentials of a kilovolt (1000 volts) or more may destroy any connected electronic or electrical equipment. The safest place in a storm is inside a metal-bodied automobile. Experimenters are advised to make themselves familiar with the resuscitation techniques for use after electric shock.

Preface

In a highly technological age, such as the time we now live in, we are surrounded by many electronic devices, which manage the even most basic everyday operations, where they can be useless or useful. We are so used to this presence, so we consider it part of the environment we see every morning on waking up.

Telecommunication development is certainly one of the main focal points of this revolution: from telephones to radio communications, from Internet to satellite navigation, from TV to space explorations with Earth controlled probes; there is no doubt that the single human's horizon is much larger. It is clear that we are connected in real time to everything that happens on our planet. We still have to see how much this can help improve our self knowledge. We will let philosophers and sociologists consider that.

After all this is said, the idea of listening to natural radio signals - those that are not emitted by a man standing somewhere, or a radio speaker or a modem - leaves us a little disorientated. Today, when we talk about radio signals, we mean the TV, radio, mobile phones, remote controls, or other communication systems linked to something technological.

Nature gives us a powerful device, the radio signal, to observe what is around us. We must be careful not to forget that most of the advanced knowledge we have today about the universe comes from observations done with radio telescopes, and not with observations in an optical field.

Even our planet is a radio signal source, mainly at low frequencies: every one of us has, at one time, listened to crackly radio noises on the medium wave during a storm! Different natural phenomena such as Auroras, earthquakes and storms create radio signals and these signals can be studied with very simple and cheap devices. The particular sound of these signals makes them unique and very fascinating. They deserve a precise definition: "Radio Nature".

Unfortunately, the advanced technology which is in all of our houses has its bad side: many of the objects we use are so complex and contain so many hours of scientific research that they become "black boxes" and we use only the final functions. In a mobile phone, for instance, we only use a set of fifteen buttons and we have no idea of what happens inside it; if we were to be transported suddenly onto a desert island, we would never be able to make one of them, but then even a seller or a constructor, or a repairman would not be able to make one the these devices.

It couldn't be different! We've lost the direct physical contact with what surrounds us. We just have to think of the objects that meant technology for our grandparents. Let's think of the old wooden cuckoo wall-clock, very complicated and full of cogs. What happened inside the clock was directly visible; springs, cogs, mechanical movements; no micro-technology, no software or program release versions.

It seems like scientific research by the individual belongs to the past or that it is possible only in hyper-technological environments; thankfully this is not true! The availability of very cheap, but powerful devices, such as the computer, makes possible today home experiments that once were done only in university settings where financial support was available. The contents of this book will show how this is now possible.

This book was born from the experience of an amateur radio operator, who very quickly diverted from long distance communication (DX) to the study of Radio Nature. The following pages include a description of these signals, an explanation of how they originate and how to build a receiving station.

Whilst describing the physical environment where these signals develop and propagate, I will mention other kinds of emissions which are not really "natural". For instance, signals generated from the mains network (better known as electromagnetic pollution in ELF band) or very low frequency emissions for submerged submarines etc. I will describe how these emissions originate and how to recognize them when they are received.

This book doesn't pretend to be a complete tutorial about naturally originating radio signals. Every subject covered in this book could fill another book. There are very deep academic studies about these topics, done by researchers who dedicate their existences to this activity. Internet technology enables us to access these publications at any time and from home.

The objective of this book is to offer a panoramic view of this fascinating subject, support for those who have no knowledge of this subject and yet, at the same time, do not wish to spend months in reading scientific books in an attempt gain an understanding. To this end we will talk about the main sources, and the propagation of natural radio signals, by simplifying, sometimes with simple analogies, the more complicated concepts, which are at the foundation of the birth of these signals. For this reason, I have chosen not to include mathematical equations to explain these physical phenomena: the very few formulas used are very simple and they have a practical use during the listening and the study of the recording.

The undoubted fascination of these signals, together with their very clear way of originating, have attracted the attention of particular type of "scientific" thought. The resemblance of some signals to human moans and to spectral whistles, have done the rest. For this reason some people have connected these signals to extraterrestrial beings and to thought transmission from this to another world; who wouldn't like to have such experience? It is certain that every time we approach a new topic, we should have no prejudice, especially when we do not have much information about the subject!

There is, however, a very big difference between having an open mind and having the strong wish to believe in something in what we want to believe.

In this book we don't talk about spirits or extraterrestrial contacts, nor telepathy: after dozens of years of recording there is no certain proof about "life" after death. Does this make the subject rational and boring? Not when you approach a subject in a scientific way, in this case the reality can be more exciting than fantasy!

Index

1. What is Radio Nature?

By Radio-Nature we mean all those electromagnetic signal emissions which originate from natural phenomena, such as storms, aurora, solar wind and other events.

We know about the electricity and noise in a thunderstorm, but we are usually unaware that a huge amount of radio waves are emitted as well. Lightning sounds and optical effects are perceived by our senses from a distance of dozens kilometers. Radio waves generated from these events can travel for thousands kilometers and they can escape from the containment of the ionosphere which surrounds our planet. They can also travel into Space guided by the terrestrial magnetic field lines of the geomagnetic field, and they can enter again returning to the surface of the Earth. With the study and experimentation of Radio Nature, we will discover that although the environment is apparently silent, it is not quiet at all in the radio spectrum.

Radio waves

We have lived with radio waves all our lives and we are so used to their presence, that by now nobody asks about their nature, except for those who have investigated them. Let us give a short definition. A radio wave has two forms of energy: electrical and magnetic. These two components are tightly connected and this relationship allows us to explain the propagation of this energy into space very far from the originating point.

The journey traveled by the energy of radio waves can have very different characteristics, which basically depend on their wavelength (and hence their frequency) and the transmitting antenna. Radio waves of the frequency used for TV transmissions, behave like light, and the transmitting and receiving antennas, must be able to 'see' each other - line of sight. Alternatively, signals such as those emitted from medium wave broadcast stations can go over hills or round very tall buildings.

Radio signals can also be reflected by obstacles. These are used in radar in order to locate the position of vehicles and other objects from a distance, or else to monitor a hill susceptible to landslides. Other radio signals - those that are not reflected back to Earth by the ionosphere - are used to observe the sky by radio astronomy. Thus the radio wave can have many different properties allowing its use for many different applications.

The base-band signals

Whilst the signals which are familiar to us, such as broadcast transmissions, are i, for instance, the FM band, Radio Nature emissions occur in base-band. Let us see what this means.

Inside a typical audio studio the speaker's voice hits the microphone and the microphone transforms the sound wave into an electric signal with the same characteristics as the sound wave. This electric information can be recorded on a tape and then reproduced from a loudspeaker, more or less accurately, according to the fidelity of the stereo system. Such a signal is called base-band: the band of frequencies is the same of the one in the voice and goes from some dozens of Hertz to some kHz. It is also known as the audio band. Usually we think of audio band frequencies from 20Hz to 20kHz, and those are the same numbers we usually find on the technical labels of the 'Walkman' and other music devices.

An example of signals propagating in base band is when during a concert, microphones, guitars, and electric pianos, all producing signals in the audio frequency range, are mixed, amplified, and then dispensed through the loudspeaker.

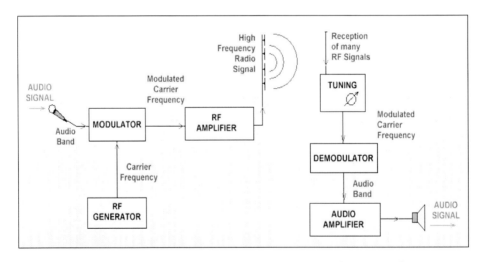

Diagram of a classical carrier frequency transmission, used in radio broadcasting.

In the situation where we have to transmit a signal over a greater distance, we need a more complex system. The audio signal is normally modulated on to a much higher frequency signal, which is then able to transport it. This transporter signal is called the carrier frequency, and it is radiated by the antenna. During the reception the carrier frequency, is received and separated from the other similar signals (tuning operation); then the original audio band is extracted again from the carrier and is sent to a loudspeaker in order to be reproduced.

The reason why we do not directly send the audio signal (in base-band) to the antenna, but use a carrier, is very simple. In order to radiate a frequency of 100MHz, to transport some music (typical of a small broadcast FM station) an antenna of less then a meter length, and some thousands of watts are sufficient. If we wish to directly radiate the signal in base-band, over the same distance, we would need a vertical antenna of dozens kilometres high, and some millions of watts. This is because of the wavelength of the base-band radio signals. Low radio frequencies have wavelengths up to hundreds of kilometres and the antenna dimensions, which must be proportional to the wavelength, become practically impossible.

There is another reason why base-band signals are not transmitted. Many signals would all overlap, and it would not be possible to separate and discriminate between the different signals. In a single area, such as a city, there could only be a single transmitting station, otherwise we would receive and listen to everything transmitted simultaneously. It would be like being in a city square or a stadium, where all the people shout at the same time, everyone towards everyone else. It would be impossible to make any sense out of it.

This is the reason why the audio frequency signals are sent on wires without any problem, traveling dozens of kilometers with very low attenuation. The most common example is analog telephone lines, where every signal goes on a separate pair of copper wires up to exchange (central office), independently without mixing up with the other ones. Every subscriber (in base-band) has their own wire. This long preamble, explains that we can transmit a signal, even at low frequencies, but it is not that convenient for entertainment or communications. This is the reason why radio signals are transmitted at higher frequencies (designated from long-waves to microwaves) and also this is why low frequency signals travel by wire (designated very long waves).

All this does not mean that there are no receivable signals at low frequency. Nature, which has abundant energy, generates most of its signals in the low bands. During a storm, every lightning flash releases millions of radio frequency watts, and most of this energy is concentrated in the audio frequency band. This peculiarity makes listening to Radio Nature very fascinating, because the sounds we listen to in the loudspeakers are really the representation of the signals generated by the storm, without needing any frequency conversion.

Radio Nature band

The following table shows the band position of natural radio signals, together with the most well known emissions.

ITU Band	Name	Extended	Frequency range	Wave length	Signals
-	SLF	Super low frequencies	Below 3 Hz	More than 100000 km	Geomagnetic pulsations
1	ULF	Ultra low frequencies	3 - 30 Hz	100000-10000 km	Schumann resonances, brain electrical activity, seismic precursors and military tests
2	ELF	Extremely low frequencies	30 - 300 Hz	10000-1000 km	Natural radio signals, submarine communications, electrical supply network harmonics
3	VF	Voice Frequency	300 - 3000 Hz	1000-100 km	Natural radio signals, electrical supply network harmonics
4	VLF	Very low frequencies	3 - 30 kHz	100 - 10 km	Natural signals and military communications
5	LF	Low frequencies	30 - 300 kHz	10 - 1 km	Long wave broadcast and other services
6	MF	Medium frequencies	300 kHz - 3 MHz	1 km – 100 m	Medium wave broadcast and other services
7	HF	High frequencies	3MHz - 30 MHz	100 m – 10 m	Shortwave broadcast and other services
8	VHF	Very High Frequencies	30 MHz - 300 MHz	10 m - 1 m	Television, Radio and other services
9	UHF	Ultra High Frequencies	300 MHz - 3 GHz	1 m - 10 cm	Television, Radio, Cellular telephones and other services

Radio Bands where we can listen to natural radio signals, with wavelength and how they are used. The bold entries are the ones we will examine in this book

Usually when we talk about VLF receiver, for Radio Nature we mean the audio frequency range between 20Hz to 20kHz. The wording in this particular case is inappropriate, because the frequency range of signals in the audio band concerns not only VLF, but ULF, ELF; and VF also. The term VLF is usually used by natural radio enthusiasts, and it is used to indicate this kind of listening.

In this book, different types of listening will be covered by their use of different reception techniques rather then by band subdivision. This is done in order to explain the practical and operational aspect of the Radio Nature listening activity. It is more useful to start from the receiving device, and then to examine what signals it is possible to explore, than to start talking about radio signals which may require a specialized receiver.

Starting from chapter three the study of Radio Nature signals is divided in three big groups:

1) **Audio band signals,** in other words, the signals receivable with a simple receiver device and listened to by the human ear using headphones or a loudspeaker, with no need for a computer to verify the presence of the signal. These signals cover a range from 100Hz to 20kHz in frequency, and by using a normal recorder or PC audio card they can be stored for eventual analysis.

2) **Subsonic band signals,** covers those signals in between 1Hz and 100Hz which are sub-audible and require the help of a graphical display on a PC to be revealed. The receiver can be the same as for (1), but our ear, even if is able to hear signals between 30 and 100Hz, is practically unable to distinguish the different characteristics. The PC audio card is a suitable means of detection.

3) **Static fields and very slow signals.**

They are not audible to the human ear because they are too slow and they cannot be displayed directly by the PC audio card. To reveal the presence of these signals we need special devices, both for reception and for acquiring on the PC.

The approach is gradual, leaving the more technically complex to the end.

The electric ears

Despite all that we said, we can see that receivers constructed to listen radio nature are very different from the ones used to receive normal radio emissions. In a Radio Nature receiver all demodulation operations, the separation of the carrier from the modulating signal, are unnecessary. The signal that will be received is already in base band. You just have to receive it with an antenna, and then transform the radio frequency wave into an electric signal, and amplify it enough to drive a loudspeaker or headphones.

A Radio Nature signal receiver is basically just an audio amplifier, with low noise and high gain, but it remains just a simple audio amplifier. The first thing we notice is the simplicity of the construction. Home made radio projects are often full of problems because of the need to receive high frequencies, but here these are not present. The main characteristic, which distinguishes this kind of receiver from a common FM radio, is that there is no tuning control. Because all of the base-band is listened to, tuning is not necessary; the only control needed is for the volume.

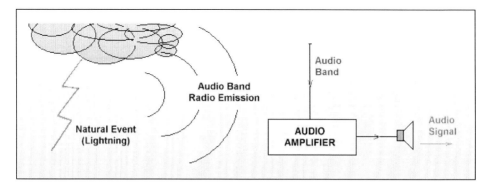

Diagram of a natural origin radio emission and its reception

With a natural origin radio signal receiver you can listen to the same frequencies you can get with a microphone. While the microphone responds to mechanical vibrations from the air around, a radio nature receiver, collects the radio (electric) signals present in the environment. It is as though we are endowed with a very sensitive electric ear, which is able to receive the "voice" of some phenomena. This electric voice can sometimes be very different from the sounds we are used to hearing.

Natural and man made signals

VLF waves contain a huge quantity of signals, many of them are of natural origin (born from meteorological events) but many of them are of artificial (man-made) origin. In this latter group, there are two main categories: signals emitted as collateral effects of the use of electrically powered devices (such as monitor, TV, drill) usually called low frequency electric noises, and on the other side, signals radiated intentionally by human beings for particular purposes.

Let us first introduce artificial signals generated in a deliberate way. In the preceding section we said that the VLF band is not suitable for radio broadcasting, and this is true. Particular physical characteristics of low frequency radio waves make them become more interesting for other purposes. VLF signals, even if difficult to transmit, will allow complete coverage of large part of a territory, or even almost all the Earth from a single transmitting station.

The large size of these waves enables them to travel beyond very big obstacles, such as mountains, making them receivable almost anywhere. What is more, they are also able to penetrate the surface of the sea and so they are able to send information where all other radio signals are blocked. We are talking now about military applications!

In fact our planet has the most important transmitting radio stations (in terms of power and dimensions) in VLF band and we will see how they work.

2. Obstacles to reception, and how signals can be displayed

Noises disturbing Radio Nature

From this short introduction we can deduce the first difficulty, which is very well known by natural origin signal researchers. The signals are not technically difficult to receive, but they are in most of the cases full of environmental noises from electric lines, TV, hairdryers, computers etc, and every possible electrically powered device.

Even the most complicated of receivers is not able to receive any natural radio signals in an apartment or a home balcony without big noises and buzzes. It is simple to discover what a silent and electrically quiet environment is. Walking in the fields alone at night, holding a receiver in our hands and wearing headphones will be the first demonstration of your passion for Radio Nature. This will probably be enough to make your neighbours ask themselves if you are sane.

You will be surprised to discover the "electric voice" of some everyday products we usually use at home such as a simple light switch or your PC monitor. The screen of your TV set will generate a noise similar to ten electric tools working very hard, and changing channel is as if all these ten machines changed their kind of work all at once. Of course this occurs even if the TV loudspeaker is at zero volume. While the TV line-scan signal at 15625Hz (in Europe) of the same TV set can be received up to hundreds of meters away. If the listening site is in an apartment block it is easy to imagine how many TV sets are switched on nearby. You will soon realize why you have to go to an open and quite space.

Electric power-lines, radiate a huge quantity of signals in the audio band, first caused by signals at 50/60Hz, which is the distribution frequency of the electric power. They also radiate many harmonics which may be generated by their users. Normally if you try to "listen" at home (if you've been able to switch off every TV set), you can just hear a large buzz, caused by mains network and by the harmonics (mainly odd): 150, 250, 350Hz (180, 300 …for US) and so on up to over 10kHz. It seems that around every electrical conductor we can see a kind of cloud of noises, some metres wide. Our houses, are full of electric conductors and become like a cage, so to do our Radio Nature listening it is necessary to get out of this cage, and go to an open space far away from electric power-lines and from the "noise cloud".

The picture on the left shows a house in a very quiet place on a hill. The picture on the right shows the hum noise situation caused by the electric power distribution. In the foggy area the hum noise overcomes the natural radio background.

High voltage lines, transporting large quantities of electric power, are big VLF band noise generators. It is possible to listen to the buzzing of a high voltage line some kilometres distance from it. By tolerating a certain quantity of noise, radio nature listening becomes possible very close to this noise, where the "noise cloud" is more rarefied.

From these statements we can deduce something scientific. The audio band range of radio frequencies brings very interesting and normally unknown signals, but if we had electric ears we would probably be deafened, and to sleep in silence we should need to go into a field or into a cave. This has not been happening for a long time. Just a couple of hundreds of years' leap back in time would be enough to experience the electric calm everywhere. Our ancestors lived in a world with the electric audio band totally clear of man-made signals, with natural origin radio signals only.

This can make you think about a return to natural living, and about a natural environment that is not electrically polluted or biologically stressed. On the Internet there are lots of offers of health generators working with natural radio wave frequencies or other things as we will see later. The very first comment we can make is that there is no direct scientific connection between VLF noise in our houses and emotional human conditions. If this kind of environment pollution was in some way noxious we would probably been extinct some seventy years ago, around the time the electric power entered our houses.

Obstacles to receiving Radio Nature

Another limitation to Radio Nature reception comes from physical obstacles. Radio Nature reception is achieved usually with electric field receivers, those which have a small rod receiving antenna. These receivers, which are very simple to construct, are sensitive to the electrical component of the signal. The electrical component is weakened by the physical screening of the environment, and here we mean those elements that we can consider to be electrical conductors. A steel framed house becomes an obstacle to the signals. This is the reason why on the balcony of our house we can only receive weak signals if we have switched off the power to avoid the disturbing noises we have talked about in the preceding paragraph.

For the same reason we would not be able to have good reception when listening in a wood, because trees are full of water and mineral salts and they become so electrical conductive that they block the reception.

The shadow effect demonstrated: near the conductive things the electric field is reduced.

For checking the presence of obstacles of this kind we can introduce the "shade effect" rule. We can assert that every conductor acts like a kind of umbrella or little tent. From the top imagine a cone producing a shaded zone. Inside of this zone signals are attenuated increasingly as we approaching the obstacle. This is an important consideration, in particular when you decide to put a receiver in the garden. The proximity of other buildings or the presence of high trees can make for a poor listening zone.

It is also very important to understand why all this physically happens. Trees, and electrical conductors become a continuation of the ground. At the top of the highest leaves we have the same electrical potential we have in the ground, and we perceive this during storms when lightning chooses the shortest path to hit the ground, that is through the top of the trees, which are the closest point at the ground potential.

To listen at VLF with an electric field receiver under two trees is like being deep in a well, as deep as the trees are tall.

Graphic representation of the signals

If you dedicate your time to a scientific activity, sooner or later you will feel that you must document the work you have done, and so you will need a graphic representation of the material you have collected. Before continuing to describe the receivable signals and how they are formed, let us briefly talk about this matter in order to understand the graphics that are used to represent these signals.

This topic will be covered in more detail later. In this chapter we will learn, the basics of associating a sound to its graphic representation, and to recognize it properly. Let us try to do this without thinking about the underlying mathematical principles.

First let us see how a word we know is graphically represented and how it can express its characteristics. We are now talking about voice recognition systems used by the police, and often seen in TV police films, where the guilty party is found by his "voice print" during a telephone call.

Time domain representation of a signal

This graph shows how our signal varies the intensity with time. In the following picture we see the representation of the words "Radio Natura" (sorry: it has been read in Italian). The graph shows us the signal duration, the oscillations and their amplitudes. It is composed of many points describing how the signal changes, or how the intensity of the signal varies with time.

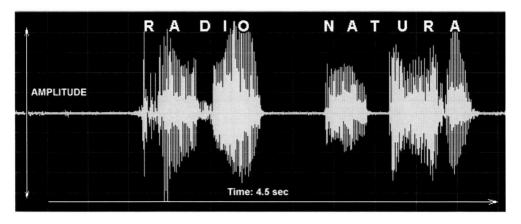

"Radio Natura" read into a microphone and analyzed with an audio card. Vertical axes represents the amplitude, horizontal axes the time.

The letters in the graph are located right where are their sounds are made. We can notice that where D and T letters are, the graph shows a reduction in sound intensity because these letter are quiet and the breath is held back. This kind of display is very similar to what we can observe in an oscilloscope. It is also called an oscillogram, since it is based on an oscillatory representation of the signal.

This is very simple to obtain, directly from an oscilloscope, or with a PC by using an audio card (soundcard). It's not very representative, though, because very different signals, but of similar amplitude, look the same with this kind of analysis.

Frequency domain representation: the spectrum

The next graph shows us both the frequency components of the signal and their intensity.

In the following picture we see the frequency spectrum of the same words, "Radio Natura" used above. The picture shows the average of both words. We can in fact observe that the zone containing most energy is the one on the left part of the graph, that is the region of the vocal frequencies, the one called the "phone band", between 300Hz and 3400Hz.

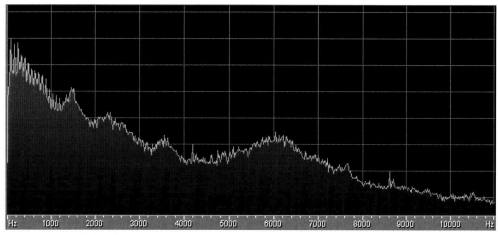

The same word Radio Natura, analyzed by frequency. Here the letters are not reported because the graph represents the average of the two words.

Amplitude changes are not displayed, but despite that, this kind of graph sometimes gives more information than an oscillogram. A spectrum, with equal amplitude signals can be very different, but we are able distinguish more easily one signal from the other, particularly when signals are complex and mixed like for instance the human voice. This display is similar to what we see in graphic equalizers, in Hi-Fi sets when they have graphics spectrum bars.

The specific instrument for analyzing the frequency composition of a signal is called a spectrum analyzer (in our case, of the audio type). This same kind of display can be seen on the PC by using the sound-card, which acquires the signal and has a specific program to process the signal and do the analysis.

Mixed time/frequency representation: the spectrogram (or waterfall display)

If, instead of doing a single spectrum analysis for the whole word, we do several sequential analyses, separated from each other by a short interval, we will build a display of the spectrum variation against time. The following picture clearly shows how different spectrum stacked together make a three-dimensional image describing in a more complete way the composition of the signal.

It is certainly the most representative representation but it is not very easy to read. One more three-dimensional spectrogram evolution is the plane visualization (two dimensions). In this case the different signal intensities are represented, either by grey tones, or different colours (hues) called the palette.

25

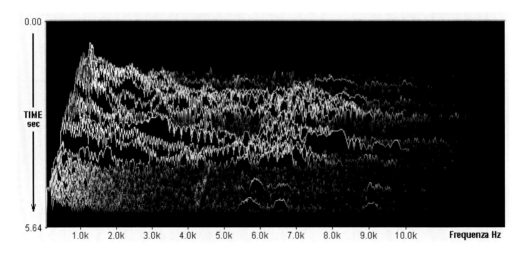

Many separate spectrums, stacked one by one, compose a 3D-spectrogram. Here representing "Radio Natura".

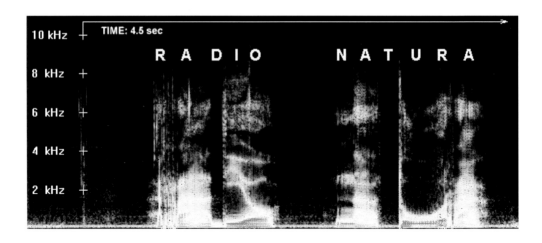

2D-Spectrogram of the words "Radio Natura". Grey tones indicate the signal strength: from black to white for weak to strong. Also here the letter position corresponds to the sound.

We have arrived! This is now the most complete representation we can get of a signal. It shows how the signal evolves in time, and in different frequency components, displaying even those weak tones, which are not perceived by the human ear.

During the 1970s the spectrogram was used almost exclusively by Universities, and the Secret Services. It was used to catalog criminals' voices, like a digital fingerprint of the voice, which is slightly different from person to person. The equipment necessary to perform these tasks was very expensive, often costing many thousands of dollars. The target signal had first to be faithfully recorded, and then processed in large and complicated analogue systems.

Today the development of PC technology and the sound-card allow this processing to be carried out in real time by anyone and at a very low cost. Software containing these kinds of analysis has been written by radio amateurs and is available free on Internet. We will return later to the deeper technical aspects and what programs are available. For the moment it is enough to know of the spectrogram function to interpret the following graphs.

3. *Terrestrial natural radio signals in the audio band*

In this important chapter we examine the principal natural radio signals originating from Earth to ionosphere, from which physical phenomena are they created, and how can we get to know them.

Electrical earth system

Our planet, electrically speaking, is very turbulent. The apparent calm, we can observe when not considering the static electric fields, seems to indicate that nothing happens in clear sky days, but measurements tell that is not so. During a storm, when this fragile equilibrium breaks, all the stored-up energy shows its most impressive side in lightning.

Even on the clearest sky days there are frequent current flows between ground and sky, but since they happen in gradual way, they are not visible, and we can record them only with appropriate equipment. By measuring the ground level electric field we can verify that, when the sky is clear, the static potential usually is around 100V/m with the soil negatively charged. This means if we had an ideal portable multimeter, we would read a value of 100V, by connecting the red probe to the ground and the black probe to the "air" at one metre high. This does not actually happen, because our meter is not ideal, because it absorbs a certain amount of the current, even though not very much. This phenomenon becomes visible and measurable with appropriate devices called electrometers, which have electrical characteristics suitable for this kind of measurement.

This static potential, which is always present, induces a very weak but continuous current flow from sky to ground. Because the air has a very high impedance, the value of this current is some billionths of an ampere per square meter. Multiplying this current flow for the whole terrestrial surface we find that the terrestrial value is enormous, about 1800 amperes! This charge could in theory neutralize the terrestrial electrical potential of our planet within a few hours, but this does not happen because of the 300 storms occurring every day on the Earth's surface, and these storms balance the continuous current. At a planetary level there are about 100 lightning strikes per second.

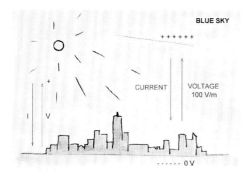 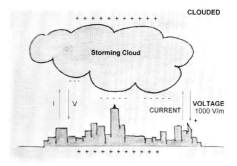

Electric field with a clear sky and clouds.

When a storm approaches the electric field reverses, going up to 1000 Volts per meter, and at the same time the current flux inverts, flowing from the Earth to the sky.

Between the lower part of storm clouds and the ground there is a difference of millions of volts. When this voltage becomes sufficient to ionize the air and to make it electrically conductive, the lightning stroke occurs. During the lightning, the current flows in the incandescent air (because of the electron movement) and approaches 10,000 amperes. Unfortunately we know their devastating effects. Lightning is the source of one of the most famed natural radio signals, "static" or the "spheric".

Static or Spherics

Their dual names derive from their origin: "static" from static discharges or lightning; "spherics" from a contraction of the English word atmospheric which means an atmospheric phenomena. The discharge (the lightning) which constitutes the radiating antenna, is of very small dimensions compared to the wavelength. So the radio emission happens in a uniform way in space, as if the signal were transmitted from a small spot in the center of a sphere, and having the same intensity over all the surface of the sphere. From here comes the second definition of spheric. Statics are the radio signal radiated by lightning and they are very common in nature, as you can imagine. They are electromagnetic emissions, with a broad spectrum, and they have the majority of their energy concentrated just in audio frequencies, or in the VLF band.

Their energy, in reality, does extend higher in frequency. If we think of shortwave or medium wave broadcasts, where we listen to amplitude modulation, the crashes of static become so numerous and so strong as the storm gets closer, that we sometimes have to abandon listening.

Statics received with an electric-field receiver for natural origin radio signals sound like the noise made by a dust on an old vinyl disk, or like the breaking of a dry wooden cane. A positive aspect of these signals is the presence of many of them. Because there is always a lot of lightning somewhere on the Earth, the statics are always receivable everywhere. It is understood that, after the first few kilometres, the lightning radio signal propagates by ground wave, following the Earth's curvature for thousands of kilometres. Wherever we are, we will always be able to receive statics to confirm that our receiver is correctly working.

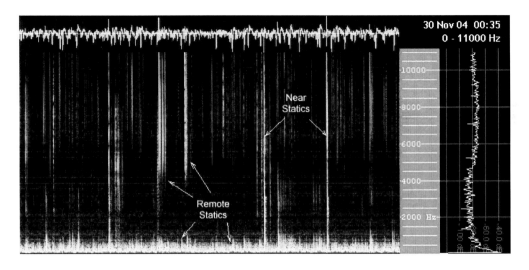

Composite analysis of remote and close statics: The Spectrogram is the large area, signal amplitude the strip at the top and frequency spectrum on the right.

The picture shows graphically what statics look like. On the oscillogram (the top part) we can clearly see that the signals are impulsive and short, while the spectrogram shows that the radiated radio energy, in such a short time, has a broad spectrum, with components at every frequency.

Static discharges are not all the same. The ones that come from few hundred kilometres away, have a uniform spectrum, with components of similar amplitude at all frequencies. In the spectrogram they appear in vertical stripes uniform in colour, from few Hz to 20kHz. After travelling several hundreds or thousands of kilometers, the statics have more energy at medium frequencies (around 5kHz) and they have more attenuated components at both low (few hundred Hz) and high (above 10kHz) frequencies. On the spectrogram they look like vertical lines, intense in the center and fuzzy away from the center.

Certainly if the propagation paths are long, this can provoke other distortion. It sometimes happens that statics appear like intermittent lines, caused by following multiple paths, the signal arriving at the receiver add or subtract depending on the differences in phase or the frequency.

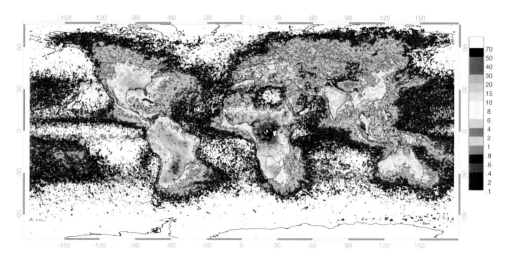

Planetary lightning map for one year. This map represents the storm activity from April 1995 to February 2003. Generated by NASA OTD and LIS instruments.
Source: http://thunder.msfc.nasa.gov

In wintertime mainly long distance statics are received, coming from tropical zones or coming from invisible discharges inside the clouds, without creating a real storm. Their intensity is usually weak. In summertime they can reach rather high radio levels, and so they can saturate receivers used to listen for them.

Statics listening can give an idea about storm activities in progress. In summertime you can foretell an incoming storm, when the sky is still totally clear, by listening to the statics generated by the event which may be occurring some hundreds kilometres away.

Maps have been available on the Internet for several years now, which show, in real time, the storm situation over the whole planet. On a search engine, it is enough to look for "storm map", to find several sites. In the last chapters I will provide a list of links. In this way, it is possible to monitor the electrostatic activity of our continent or the area we live in and also to understand where these signals come from.

Tweeks

These are a deformation, or a distortion the static suffers when it propagates in certain specific conditions. They sound like a twittering and it seems as though it starts from the static, or from a gun shot hitting a plane surface. We can hear the static (strong shot) and at the same time a single "ciuuup" lasting about one tenth of a second. When these conditions are present every static can generate two or more tweeks and in certain circumstances there can really be a storm of tweeks, as though we are in a aviary full of birds.

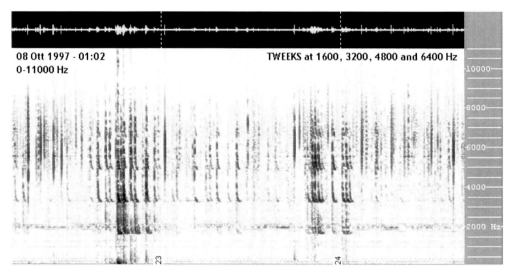

Spectrogram of 2.5 sec with multiple tweeks, received in Cumiana (NW Italy). The hooks are visible at 1600, 3200, 4800 and 6400Hz.

Graphically, a tweek looks like a hook shape coming all of a sudden out of the static, usually at a couple of kilohertz, almost as if the static was bent. When the atmospheric conditions are favorable, we can find double frequency harmonics, or triple or even quadruple, "hooking" of the static at different points spaced by the same frequency interval. When this happens the tweek effect is amplified and resonates producing a continuous sound as if we were listening with our ear to a bottle.

Tweeks are created by the static signal "bouncing" from the highest ionosphere layer, and it is reflected in an anomalous way. The signal travels over a longer path at lower frequencies and there is a slowing down at these low frequencies in comparison to the higher ones, caused by multiple reflections in a single ionospheric layer. We will describe this process, called "dispersion", in detail in a later section, when talking about whistlers.

It seems that the tweeks' dispersion originates from radio wave interaction with the terrestrial magnetic field at the ozone layer, about sixty kilometers from the ground. To be generated, tweeks must travel two thousand kilometers from the starting stroke. We can receive them at night-time only and preferably in wintertime rather than summertime. They depend on the ionospheric conditions being right, and statics being present. They really are a very common signal to listen to.

The insects (Buzzer)

This is a very particular signal, like a couple of bees nervously flying in a closed room.

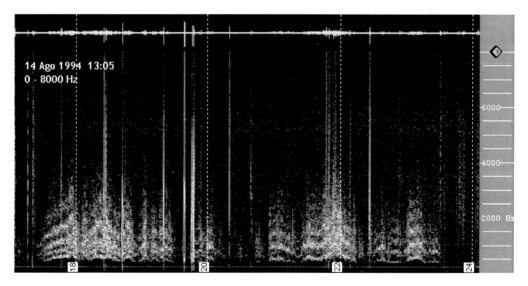

Spectrogram 7 seconds long represents a buzzer. Received in "Pian dell'Alpe", 1950m high in NW Italy.

There really are no insects close to the receiver or the antenna. This signal is produced by the current flowing between clouds and ground, induced by the potential difference. When this is higher than a certain value, small channels in the air are created, where current flows noisily creating this particular electrical noise. It is usually composed of a time varying base frequency and some harmonics of decreasing amplitude as the frequency gets higher. It lasts just a few minutes or hours depending on electrical conditions of the sky. We can easily listen to them if we are on the top of a mountain, or even sometimes in a plain, but mainly when the sky is cloudy, with low clouds.

This one is different from the others, it is a more local signal we can find only within a few kilometers radius of the listening point and it does not really propagate very far.

4. *Extra-terrestrial natural radio signals in the audio band*

Do not misunderstand this title: we are *not* talking about aliens, UFOs, or extra-terrestrial creatures. We are simply talking about signals originating from natural physical phenomena occurring outside the terrestrial ionosphere that surrounds the Earth, called the magnetosphere. We are talking about the area encircling our planet for several thousands kilometres, where the magnetic field effect of our planet is still intense enough to form a zone where solar and cosmic-ray particles are slowed down by collision processes. Helium nuclei, protons and electrons, coming from the sun are trapped, forming a kind of fat ring around the earth. The regions occupied by this "bun" are called the Van Allen belts by astrophysicists.

Graphical representation of solar wind and its effect on the terrestrial magnetic field.

Our magnetic field protects us from the harmful effects of solar wind.

Reproduced with NASA authorization.

Source: http://scijinks.jpl.nasa.gov /weather/

The magnetosphere is deformed by the solar wind and it is squeezed on the solar side of our planet with a long tail in the other side. The illuminated side can extend for dozen of Earth radii, while the opposite part is more than a hundred Earth radii.

Whistlers

This kind of signal is certainly one of the most fascinating, both for its sound and for the way it is generated. We do not know who first noticed its existence. It may be American long distance phone line technicians, who found it in their headphones, without knowing how to explain what they heard on the wires, which were working as an antenna.

Or, it may be that it was discovered by during the World War I using long trench telephone lines. Some very secret transmissions from trench to trench used ground telegraphic currents and they did not use classical radio frequencies, which were capable of being intercepted by the enemy. The recipient received the signal by picking up the potential difference between two grounds stakes and amplifying it with a vacuum tube (the system worked like a VLF receiver).

The "hissing waves", or "whistlers", sound like whistles decreasing in frequency and lasting from half a second to several seconds. You can mimic it by emitting whistle for some seconds, starting from the highest frequency you can make, and slowly descending to low frequencies. This is a "home made" but real reproduction of what you hear when you receive a "hissing wave".

The way these signals originate is fascinating and is strictly connected to the statics we've talked about earlier. Part of the energy travels via the groundwave (as with the medium and long radio broadcast waves) and propagates for thousands of kilometers from the point of the lightning discharge. Another part is trapped and reflected several times in the ionospheric night time layer and this creates the tweeks. Finally part escapes, going up vertically from the point where the electric discharge had begun and starts to disperse into the space.

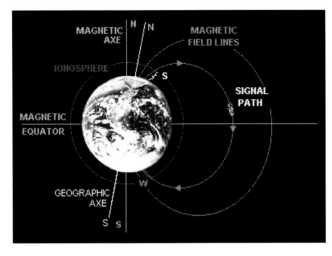

Origin, propagation and reception of a whistler: the wave path follows the terrestrial magnetic field lines

The magnetosphere is the space surrounding the Earth where magnetic fields exist because of the Earth's magnetism. In particular conditions, with high values of solar wind, the discharges radiated into space cannot move freely any longer and they cannot radiate in a direct way so they are guided along the magnetic field lines, following invisible ducts that bring them back to the Earth at the geomagnetic conjugate point. The geomagnetic conjugate points correspond to zones crossed by the same magnetic field lines, as if the Earth were a big magnet.

As a practical example, the geomagnetic conjugate point for southern Europe corresponds to South Africa. In other words, the point where the magnetic line of force leaves southern Europe is magnetically jointed to the point where the line re-enters in Africa. In suitable conditions, a lightning discharging in Africa can radiate its signal (the static) through this great distance and can arrive in Europe, and vice versa. The original static travels for thousands kilometers in space, and because of this long distance, it suffers the phenomenon called dispersion, where the higher frequencies arrive first, while lower ones are slowed down and arrive a few seconds later. The result is fascinating: when the original South African static (sounding like a whip-crack) arrives in Europe it becomes a whistle ("fiiiiuuu") very far from its resemblance to the original signal.

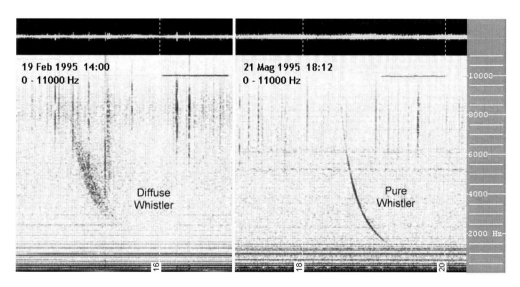

A three-second spectrogram shows a diffuse whistler and a pure whistler. They were received in Cumiana (NW Italy). We can also see weak statics, some hum noises and a 10kHz tone of the Omega Navigation Network (no longer active).

Whistlers are easy to receive because they are a rather strong signal but, at the same time, they are quite rare at medium latitudes. Starting from the poles and arriving to the equator, the possibility of receiving the hissing wave becomes more and more rare. It is still possible to do this kind of listening on most parts of the

37

path. This does not mean that a couple of listening periods would be enough to capture a whistler. Sometimes several months can go by without the phenomenon occurring. Then, all at once, a few whistlers start to appear, followed by some stronger ones, then, if we are lucky within a few minutes we are in the middle of a whistler storm with rate of up to one per second.

TYPES OF WHISTLER

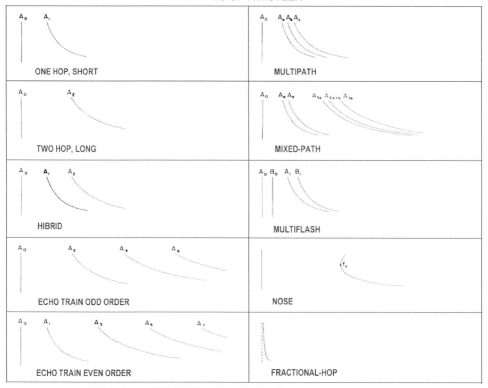

CLASSIFICATION BY PROF. ROBERT A. HELLIWELL, STANFORD UNIVERSITY, CALIFORNIA 1965

Whistler format classification, produced by Stanford University in 1965. The first line on the left (Ao) represents the signal of the original static.

Whistlers can arrive through a single duct, or they can travel through several different length paths at the same time. In the first case, the whistler arrives with a purer note and in the spectrogram it is like a curving line, very neat and thin. In the case where the static takes more simultaneous paths, on exit we will have delayed whistlers. The spectrogram display of the static will be smooth, and the whistler signal will not be so neat and sharp and it is called a diffuse whistler, to distinguish it from the first type which is called pure whistler.

The whistlers we have just talked about are all generated in a single journey, and for this reason they are called one-hop whistlers. When the ducts have good propagation characteristics, the single lightning signal can bounce backward and forward several times generating multi-hop whistlers. As soon as the hops increase, the dispersion time also increases due to the different journey travel time. For this reason the first bounce has a brief and short whistler and the following ones will have a longer and slower whistlers ("fiiiiiuuuuuuuu"). These rather rare signals are called train whistlers or echo train whistlers.

These signals can sometimes be listened to in total quietness, without any local electrostatic activity, in other words in the absence of any storms for hundreds kilometres, because their origin is thousands of kilometres away at the conjugate geomagnetic point. It is clear now that Solar conditions influence the formation of these ducts. When the Solar activity gets more intense, the formation of these special paths is easier and we can more easily receive whistlers.

Auroral chorus

These signals are themselves very fascinating, even though they are more difficult to hear at medium and high latitudes. The Auroral chorus comprises increasingy musical whistles, sometimes simultaneously and with different frequencies. These tones can vary in length, ranging from one tenth on a second to several seconds. They sound like a flock of birds, making a loud noise, or like many dogs barking all together. They can appear for few seconds and they can quickly disappear in the same manner.

Sometimes the quantity of the sounds is very large, and so it can be called a whistler storm. Chorus originates from the interaction of solar wind and our magnetosphere. The explosions occurring on the sun surface during very intense solar activity periods release energy towards our planet as radio waves, X rays (solar flux) and particle bursts (coronal mass ejections, CME, and the solar wind).

In the closest regions to the poles the solar wind and particle bursts can generate a luminous physical effect called "Aurora": "Aurora Borealis" in the Northern hemisphere and "Aurora Australis" in the Southern. This fascinating phenomenon illuminates the nocturnal sky with several coloured bands after a period of solar activity. When VLF signals are originated by this phenomenon, they are called the Auroral Chorus and they can even be very intense. At medium latitudes this phenomenon is very rare and in most cases it is only observed in the regions close to the poles. Despite this, radio signals generated by the aurora can travel beyond auroral area and they can even be received at lower latitudes.

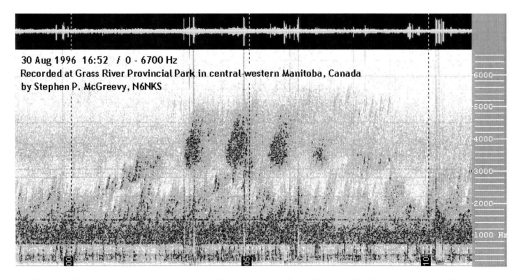

30 Aug 1996 16:52 / 0 - 6700 Hz
Recorded at Grass River Provincial Park in central-western Manitoba, Canada
by Stephen P. McGreevy, N6NKS

A 13 seconds spectrogram, showing a chorus received in Canada by the researcher Stephen McGreevy.

Although these signals can be listened to all day long and all night long, they are stronger at local sunrise. Their intensity decreases as soon as we move far from the polar regions, and at the same time, as we get closer to equatorial zones, the tones making up the chorus tend to have a higher frequency.

Auroral hisses, periodic and discrete emissions

Here we are talking about wideband emissions from hundreds of Hz to dozens of kHz. They originate, as for the chorus, from the interaction of the solar wind and our magnetosphere. The lower frequency emissions are heard closest to the auroral regions, while higher frequency ones are scattered over a huge area, with higher intensity towards poles and with a progressively decreasing strength approaching equatorial regions.

Discrete emissions are defined duration signals, lasting few seconds or even less. They can be composed of pure tones (a very well defined track on the spectrogram) or by more diffuse signals (fuzzy tracks). The most common kind are ascending tones, descending tones, and "hooks". When these signals occur repeatedly in regular way, they are called periodical emissions.

VLF EMISSIONS

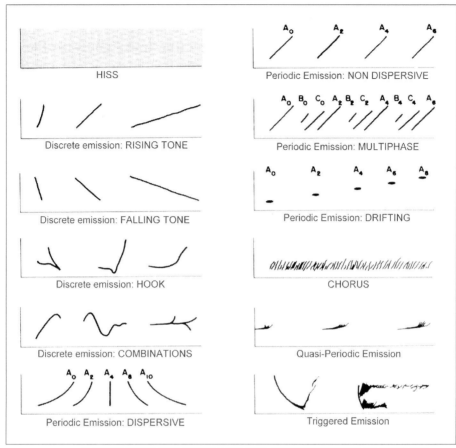

HISS

Discrete emission: RISING TONE

Discrete emission: FALLING TONE

Discrete emission: HOOK

Discrete emission: COMBINATIONS

Periodic Emission: DISPERSIVE

Periodic Emission: NON DISPERSIVE

Periodic Emission: MULTIPHASE

Periodic Emission: DRIFTING

CHORUS

Quasi-Periodic Emission

Triggered Emission

CLASSIFICATION BY PROF. ROBERT A. HELLIWELL, STANFORD UNIVERSITY, CALIFORNIA 1965

This table has been generated by Stanford University in 1965 show the main kinds of VLF emissions.

At medium latitudes, it is generally easy to listen to hisses and chorus (even if the event does not follow the rule, as for whistlers), while other types are more rare.

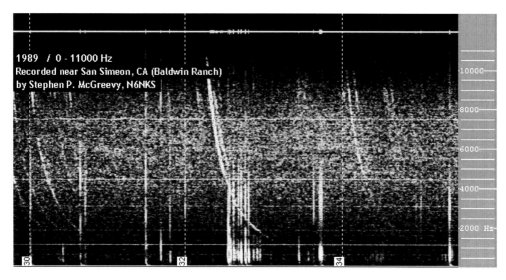

1989 / 0 - 11000 Hz
Recorded near San Simeon, CA (Baldwin Ranch)
by Stephen P. McGreevy, N6NKS

A six seconds spectrogram with a hiss, some statics and a whistler. Received by Stephen McGreevy in California.

Flying saucers

Saucers are the last type in our discussion of different types of signal. They are strictly connected to the aurora phenomenon and are usually receivable close to the low geographical aurora edge. They come from the same family of emissions as the whistlers and they have first a decreasing tone, then an increasing tone.

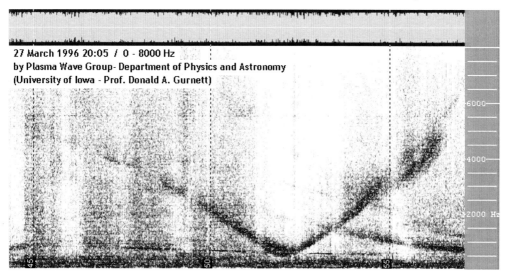

27 March 1996 20:05 / 0 - 8000 Hz
by Plasma Wave Group- Department of Physics and Astronomy
(University of Iowa - Prof. Donald A. Gurnett)

A Saucer, received from the Iowa University (US), by Prof. Gurnett's group.

The lowest frequency part is at some hundreds of Hertz, while highest parts reach and sometimes exceed 6kHz. The human ear receives a whistler first decreasing then increasing, sometimes very clear and defined, but at other times more diffuse. On the spectrogram they appear like a "V", in some cases very neat and pointed, and at other times, plain and fuzzy like a flying object. At medium latitudes those signals are very rarely received, but as soon as we move closer to the poles, we can receive them more easily.

5. *Artificial signals detectable in the audio band*

Together with radio signals of natural origin bands, we have several signals connected to human activities. It is essential to know about them in order to distinguish them from Radio Nature listening. Mistakes, during VLF monitoring, are very easy to make. It is common to confuse high voltage electro duct tones with submarine intercommunication signals. Also, it is easy to mis-identify as seismic precursors, simple temporary electric line noises. We can even misunderstand the effect of mechanical oscillation in the antenna caused by the wind and assume some other special effects. You can distinguish one from the other only with much experience. It is important to understand, however, that these artificial signals which are very often present are still a good means to test if the receiver is correctly working.

Hum noise and cyclic noises

Without doubt, power feed hum is about the most common signal in a normal domestic environment. It travels through electric wires and it normally is at 50/60Hz, its basic nominal frequency, but there are also harmonics with strong signals at the even harmonics and more importantly very strong signals at odd harmonics. This signal is called "comb", because the image on the spectrum analyzer resembles a hair-comb with the spine downward and the teeth pointing upwards. Walking around our house in Europe with an electric field receiver for natural radio signals we can find 50, 100, 150, 200, 250Hz, and so on up to 10kHz. Moving away from our house, these noises decrease and at 20 meters distance, the situation is the one shown in the right part of the following picture. At 200 meters, far from electric lines, we finally have the optimal situation, shown in the left part of the picture, where even low frequency statics are displayed and are not covered by line buzzing.

We are talking about the "cloud" of signals surrounding all electrical wires where alternating current flows and which makes listening for radio nature impossible in domestic environments, including balconies, small gardens, public avenues and country roads with public illumination. It is usually enough to get some dozens of metres away from the electric lines, to bring this noise back down to normal levels, and to be able to listen to natural signals such as the ones mentioned in the previous chapters. It sounds like a continuous noise, similar to many high speed turbines running. To avoid the hum noise totally you have to move some kilometres away from electric lines, and in heavily built-up areas near towns this can be very difficult..

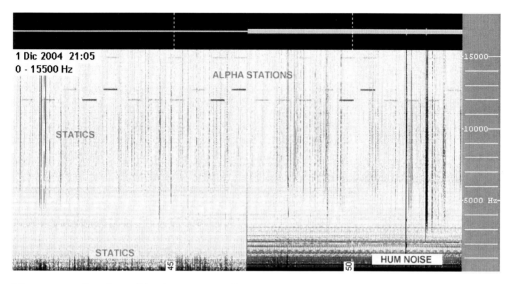

The same receiver is used in the country (left part) and in a house garden. The receiver works in both situations, but near the house the hum noise below 3kHz blocks the reception of the lower part of the spectrum.

When we are close to a house, there are some factors, which strongly increase this noise. Low energy light bulbs, for the lighting system and light dimmers, can emit harmonics up to 22kHz and more, and they are a real problem for those who are trying to listen to signals buried down in the noise.

The listening station can be located in the garden, tolerating a certain amount of hum noises, but as soon as your neighbour turns on a halogen bulb with a dimmer, you can stop your listening session for as long as that bulb is lit.

Together with mains network harmonics, we can sometimes find cyclic noises, similar to static sounds. These are regular with a periodicity of around half a second. They belong to the large group of the signals, which are carried on electricity lines as their transmission medium. They can be due to timing signals periodically inserted to control street lighting or traffic lights and they can propagate many kilometres away from the where they are generated.

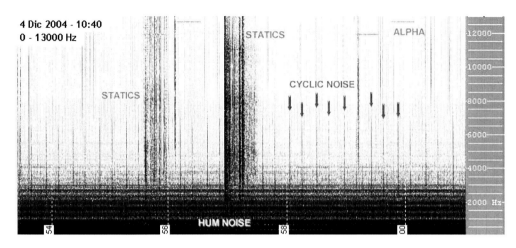

Typical reception in a garden near a house, with strong hum noise and a cyclic noise from 3 to 8kHz. Alpha and statics are receivable, but a Whistler detection can be very hard in these conditions.

All this refers to low voltage distribution lines (220/110V). For high voltage lines, the noise coverage area gets even bigger, impeding good quality reception for several kilometres. Besides normal hum noise made by multiples of 50/60Hz, some other tones appear in these cases, not always stable in frequency, and for this reason difficult to eliminate, even using DSP filter systems in the computer.

Signals from high voltage power lines

Many national high voltage power distribution lines carry control signals as well as the electric power currents. These are used by big electric service industries to control a tariff, which changes according to the hour of the day.

Receiving VLF signals 10km from a high voltage line, as is possible in southern Europe, telegraphic tones from 300 to 1300Hz are received in a clear and precise form. The signal, when first heard, seems to be transmitted in a very slow Morse code, but its coding does not correspond to any alphabet letter. What we have is the European electric companies tariff changing system, sent from the power station to the users' electric meters. They are injected onto line together with dozens of kilowatts of power. They are receivable even if the country we are living in has not yet introduced the tariff changing system, and even if the country has no 'intelligent' electricity meters yet, but only old electromechanical meters. The electricity distribution lines of many countries are connected together and these signals will cross the borders, traveling on for hundreds kilometres. In Italy, for instance, we can easily receive several sequences at 1024Hz and some others less often at 470Hz even if the national energy producer does not use them. They are usually sent on the hour or the half hour.

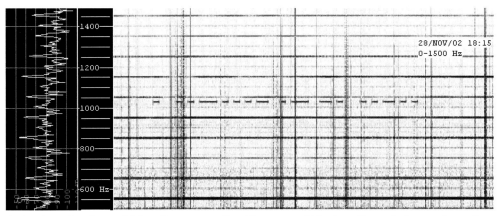

A signal coming from a high voltage power line, 2km away: This show the main harmonics and a 1024Hz signal control.

Another kind of signal travels on high voltage power lines, centered around 2kHz it is usually composed of several carriers modulated with different tones.

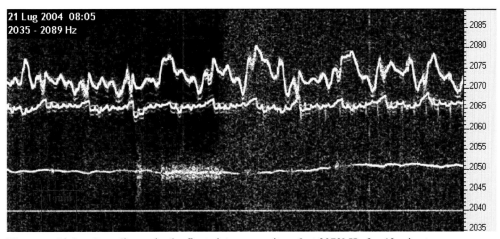

The same high voltage line as in the first picture, monitored at 2070kHz for 13 minutes.

Even if their discovery and observation is interesting, we know they are just noises or obstacles to good signal reception. We must be able to distinguish them from the wanted, natural, signals.

Electric motors

If, near your listening location, there is a mechanical workshop with lathes, or a carpenter's workshop, you may receive signals looking like the ones shown in the following spectrogram

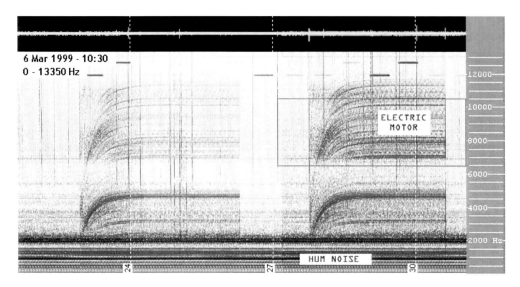

A typical comb of carriers, generated by an electric motor. Two complete working cycles are recognizable: when the motor starts, the frequency is low and rises as the motor reaches working speed, maintained for the working cycle. When the motor stops the comb disappears.

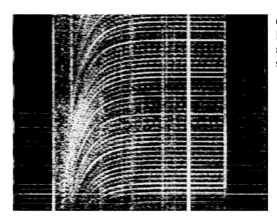

Comb generated by an electric motor: Here start and stop are characterized by a crackling noise, generated by the switch.

The noise is very similar to the one made by a drill, and electrically is made up of a central carrier frequency, which has the same value of the motor's rotational speed. Single carriers are spaced by twice the mains frequency, which is

100 or 120Hz. Because of the similar mechanism, the same effect is produced by our neighbour using a drill, and the VLF signal travels for several hundreds of metres.

Something very important emerges for the natural origin radio signals from all of this. We can discover the best place to install the receiving station. For an amateur radio operator the main problem is essentially where to place the antenna (preferably in the highest position). In the natural radio case, height is not so important, but what is most essential is to maximise the distance from electricity lines and from all the noises they carry.

The TV Line-timebase signal

Even a television receiver generates a large amount of VLF band noise. So you will have to forget VLF listening in areas close to apartment blocks during the evening. You can easily count how many televisions are switched on, and all the natural radio signals are buried under them, unless they are lightning strikes very close to you. Fortunately, most of this noise disappears after moving a few dozens of metres, and only the TV line timebase signal, also called the flyback signal, propagates over any great distance.

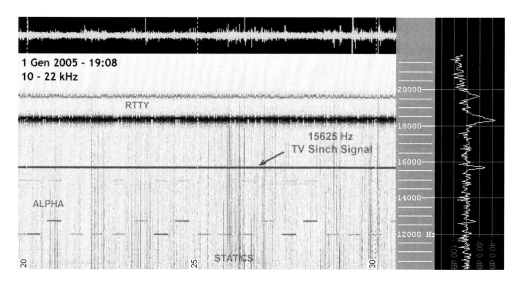

A 15625Hz tone coming from a television running 50m away. The signal emerges from a natural noise background of about 30dB.

The TV line-timebase signal is very easy to identify since the frequency is always 15,625Hz (in Europe). Whenever the remote control changes channel (that is during those brief instants when the video images are unsynchronized), the tone suffers a small frequency shift. As soon as the TV set is locked again it remains stable, locked to the chosen channel, and the frequency returns at 15,625Hz. A TV line-timebase signal, from a receiver at ground level, can propagate for more than 200 meters from the generating television set.

Alpha hyperbolic radio-navigation stations

These are VLF transmitters located in different parts of Europe or Asia. Nowadays with the coverage of GPS systems they might seem to be obsolete, but they are Russian stations used to radio navigate in the northern seas. Before GPS existed, they were one of the few possible means to establish the real, accurate ship location. With a radio receiver, which determines the difference between phase and received tones of two transmitters, it is possible to trace curves (hyperbolas) on a chart. With their intersection it is possible to calculate the ship's location on a map.

Today they are still in use, even if their use has diminished with the advancement of technology. America ran an similar system called Omega, which was switched off several years ago. The Russian system remains in use despite its very high costs and the reason is basically strategic: GPS is an American possession and, in case of war, blocking it could immobilize everything and everyone that uses this technology. With their Alfa system, called RSD 20, the Russians keep their independence and autonomy over their radio navigation system.

The Alpha signal cycle consists of a tone sequence lasting a total of 3.6 seconds. There are six frequencies, each lasting 0.4s with intervals of 0.2s following in a sequence.

Sequences periodically change (they sometimes last few days only) and use frequencies starting from 11904Hz and go up to 15625Hz. In total, nine frequencies are used derived from multiples and divisions of two basic frequencies: 744Hz and 781.25Hz, which are never themselves transmitted. The system is based on five different transmitters located in five widely spread sites. During the last few years we often have seen all of the stations turned off for several days or even for whole weeks. Officially this was done for maintenance, though it has been suggested that this was because of Russian financial difficulties.

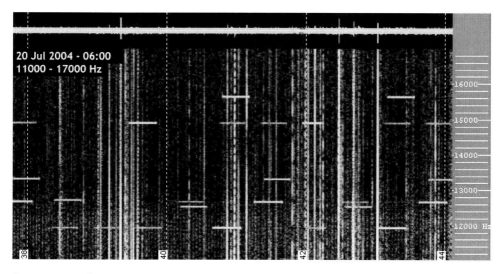

Spectrogram with two complete Alpha sequences. In this system the frequencies change often.

We have no precise data about the Russian system, but a single American Omega station cost something like 12 million dollars annually. which contributors paid in the 1980s. Physical structures to radiate such low frequency signals are obviously enormous because of the wavelength; we are talking about vertical towers more than 100 metres high with kilometres of hanging cables powered by many kilowatts of RF power.

To the human ear they sound like very sharp tones, near to a hiss, a "biii boooo" sequence. They are received very strongly all over Europe.

Military RTTY (radio teletype)

The mode of propagation of these long waves, their capability of easily rounding obstacles such as mountains or hills and the characteristic of penetrating into the upper layers of water, made them one of the most indispensable supports for military communications with worldwide coverage.

Stations radiating these signals have enormous physical dimensions. They often have a series of towers up to 427 metres high with kilometres of phosphor-bronze cables, suspended between the vertical supports and concrete counterbalances weighing several tons. The radio frequency powers used are millions of watts, and power stations are built specially to produce the current needed to power these transmitters.

In some places, where ice formation on the antennas could compromise the efficiency, transmission installations are doubled. So that while one antenna works, a twin antenna is heated by feeding it with a huge quantity of electrical energy. When the first antenna starts to get iced, the two antennas are changed over.

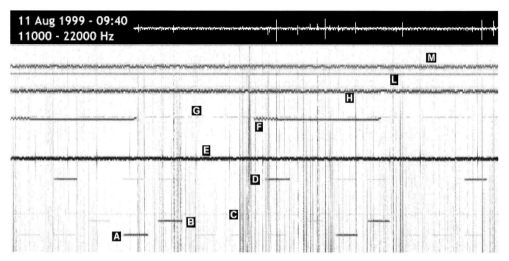

A busy morning with much traffic, recorded in Turin (NW Italy). Received stations are: A), B) and D), ALPHA radio navigation system; C) the Australian VL3DEF; E) the powerful English GBR; F) the Russian UFQE; G) the Indian VTX3, the only one transmitting in Morse code; H) the English GBZ; L) probably the Chinese 3SA; M) a Russian station.

One of the high power vacuum tubes, from the VLF station of Tavolara (Sardinia Island, Italy). It is a Machlett ML5682 triode, with 215kW continuous power output, or 8MW pulsed. The tube weight is 25kg and is water-cooled.
Picture reproduced with authorization of SPIN Electronics, Italy.

Frequency kHz	Call	Country	Location, Modulation
16.400	JXN	NOR	HELGELAND, NOVIK,MSK, 200 Bd
17.000	VTX2	IND	VIJAYANARAYANAM, MSK
17.200	SAQ	SWE	VARBERG/GRIMETON, CW
18.100	RDL	RUS	KRASNODAR, MSK, CW
			ARKHANGELSK MSK, CW
			KRASNODAR, MSK, CW
			ARKHANGELSK, MSK, CW
18.200	VTX3	IND	VIJAYANARAYANAM, MSK
18.300	HWU	FRA	LE BLANC (Rosnay), MSK
18.500	DHO35	GER	BURLAGE,RAMSLOH, MSK
19.200	VTX	IND	VIJAYANARAYANAM, MSK
19.800	NWC	AUS	H.E. HOLT/NORTH WEST CAPE/ EXMOUTH
20.270	ICV	ITA	TAVOLARA, MSK
20.500	RJH63/66/77	RUS	ARKHANGELSK, etc
20.900	HWU	FRA	SAINTE ASSISE, MSK
21.100	RDL	RUS	various, CW, MSK
21.750	HWU	FRA	LE BLANC (Rosnay), MSK

A list of some main stations receivable in the European region, extracted from the RDF PROJECT of Manfred F Kerckhoff. *(http://www-user.uni-bremen.de/~ews2/RDF_project.html)*

An OMEGA radio navigation signals receiver: model GNS500A, made by Globalnavigation.
Picture from Spin Electronics Museum, Italy.

Besides some sporadic emissions in telegraphy, when the station call is transmitted, all other transmissions are MSK modulated. The carrier frequency is shifted by some fixed frequency to form the code elements. All the messages are coded with the best and most sophisticated encryption systems.

Amateur interest in the reception of these transmissions is not for their content, impossible to decode, but for the study of radio propagation in these bands, given that frequency emissions and locations are easily traceable. These signals start from 13.0kHz: there are no RTTY transmissions below this.

Nuclear explosions

My wish is that nobody would file in his radio listening log, a nuclear explosion radio signal. These tests have been done since 1953 and even VLF radiation was part of the recorded data. We will describe the most interesting technical aspects.

A nuclear explosion produces a very strong radio signal in the VLF band with maximum intensity between 10 and 15kHz; the signal sounds more or less like a spheric generated by lightning. Between 1953 and 1962, five nuclear warheads were radio controlled and exploded. This was done in the Nevada desert 90 meters high and on Johnston Island 400 kilometers high. They were of different strengths, from few kilotons (the equivalent of thousands of tons of TNT) exploded in the desert at the California borders, to several megatons (millions of tons of TNT) exploded in a little Pacific Ocean island, thousand kilometres from Hawaii.

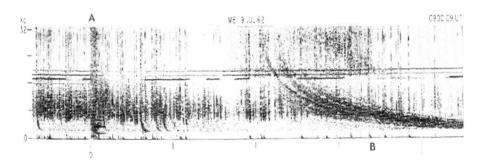

Spectrogram recorded on 9 July 1962 by Stanford University, reporting a VLF signal generated by the "Starfish" nuclear test (A) and a whistler received in New Zealand (B). The analysis recorded from 0 to 32kHz shows that a nuclear whistler is identical to a natural one.

The VLF nuclear explosion signals went out in the ionosphere and travelled following the Earth's magnetic field lines generating whistlers, similar to or even better than when a storm occurs, some double hopped and some single hopped.

The signals were monitored at seven different sites including Stanford in California, and Boulder in Colorado. The nuclear whistler created by the 9 July 1962 explosion in Pacific Ocean, called Starfish Prime, was received up to 6,800 kilometers far away in Wellington, New Zealand.

6. *False signals in the audio band*

Natural origin radio signal reception hides many traps, mostly these signals are more similar to noise than to well defined signals, such as a telegraphic transmission. It is easy to mistake a functional fault in the receiver for some exotic reception. Let us see what main the misperceptions are and how to identify them.

Cross modulation or receiver saturation

Receivers constructed to receive VLF signals, without conversion, are usually simple and designed to work in most situations. However, just as a home telephone can have problems if operates close to a mobile, these receivers can similarly be saturated if input signals are too strong. In case of signals stronger that they can bear - overload, all devices enter in a zone known as non-linearity. This can generate harmonics and spurious signals.

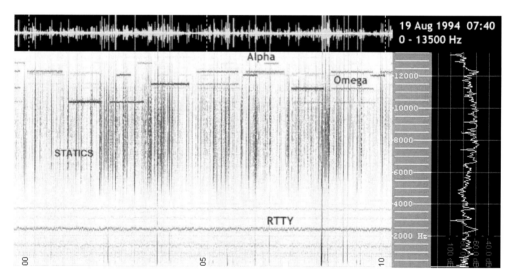

A ten second spectrogram, received on the top of Pintas Mountain (2543m high, NW-Italy) in 1994. The OMEGA stations were still active. Below 4kHz some RTTY signals appear, but they don't actually exist in that position, and they are created inside the receiver.

This can happen if the antenna used is too big and if the receiver is not well filtered; but it can also happen if we are close to a high power transmitting station or simply if the nocturnal propagation brings medium and short wave signals more strongly than the receiver can stand.

Here we are then, in the middle of listening to statics and a for few seconds we hear some exotic music or a voice talking in a mysterious language, then it quickly disappears. This effect is not only produced on voice modulated signals but also on data signals. If you are listening to a teletype at 3kHz, you can be sure that the receiver front end is overloaded, because there are no RTTY signal under 13kHz.

Sometimes the receiver sensitivity is enhanced by choice of the reception site. Received signals on a plain are much weaker than the ones received at the top of a mountain. This is the ground-plane effect, which is horizontal in the plain and pointed on the top of a mountain. A receiver, which works well on low ground, can have intermodulation problems if brought onto higher ground, and in this situation needs either a shorter antenna, or an attenuator at the front end, to reduce its sensitivity.

In many cases the intermodulation phenomenon is not produced by the receiver but by the recorder (if connected) which doesn't tolerate the wide bandwidth of the signals. The end effect is the same, and to eliminate it we need to reduce the input signal in the recorder, or we may have to put an audio filter in between the recorder and the receiver. Anyway, before attempting listening sessions in far away and uncomfortable places, it is very useful to make tests to determine what the equipment performance limits are, by using some measuring equipment.

The microphone effect

Both with a VLF electric field receiver and with a similar device sensitive to the magnetic component (we will discuss the difference between the two receivers later) we will sooner or later have to handle the microphone effect. This is a mechanical vibration applied to the antenna or the receiver, and transformed into an electric signal just like the ones we normally receive. The consequence is that the wind makes the antenna oscillate and this makes an electrical sound mixing up with the received ones. It's easy, after hours of tape recording listening, to find the presence of mysterious sound traces without being able to find out if, at that time, the weather was windy. So it is worthwhile, before every listening session, especially if it is being recorded, to shake the entire antenna-receiver system, and even better, to record the signal produced. This kind of signal depends on the receiving system mechanical resonances and so it is different for every kind of antenna and receiver. It is a mechanical "fingerprint" of that particular receiving set up.

Insects

Electric field receivers (whip antenna types) are also sensitive to the weak electrostatic field variations, which we can detect close to flying insects. The wings beating vary the charge density of the air, and this variation is received by the antenna, as a periodic signal. If a hornet or a fly gets close to the whip, the receiver picks up this weak signal and amplifies it before passing it to the recorder or to the headphones. The electrical signal produced is very similar to the one we would hear by putting our ear close to the insect. The weak electric field around the small insect is only receivable few centimeters away. Perhaps it is incorrect to define this as a "false signal" because it really is a natural emission....let us just say that usually it is not our research objective.

Garment static discharges

Children typically are fascinated by static electrical phenomena. When removing a synthetic garment in the dark (eg nightwear), it sparkles like it was electrically charged. If there were an electric field receiver near by this undressing operation, we would be surprised by the strong radio signal such a simple action can generate. There is a similar effect if we just walk. With only the garment friction, we produce an electrostatic field, which can disturb our reception. If, for instance, we walk with the receiver in our hand, we can clearly hear our trousers rubbing as though we had a microphone in our pocket.

We have to recognise this effect when planning listening sessions. It is better to place the receiver three or four metres away from the operator, or far away from where other people are.

Wristwatches and cars

Using a loop antenna with a magnetic field receiver (we will discuss its details later) we must consider two other sources of false signals. The first one is the quartz watch with mechanical hands, the second one is motor cars.

Wristwatches generate a weak VLF magnetic field, easily recognizable because it has pulses every second. The signal will come and go depending on how the magnetic field (generated by the small switch inside the watch) couples to the loop antenna. If we are in a field at night for a listening session with our loop antenna and our headphones on, we think we can hear someone walking behind us, but there is nobody. Well, next time we will have to leave our wristwatch at home.

Another rather typical noise is the vehicle ignition in petrol (gasoline) engines. If it is received with an electric field receiver, the signal will sound like a series of electric discharges, similar to static, but more with a more regular rhythym. Usually this noise does not travel more than ten meters from the point of origin. If you use a loop antenna and a magnetic field receiver, you will be able to receive the signal up to 200 meters from the vehicle. In this case, the signal is generated by currents flowing in the high voltage coil. The received sound is similar to a turbine, or to the one produced by a drill turning at the same speed of the engine. Because this last type of noise is very invasive, you have to carefully choose a listening place avoiding a queue of cars for a crowded event, so as not to confuse it with a whistler storm.

7. VLF receivers

After describing all the receivable signals in the VLF field, let us now move on to see how a natural radio signal receiver works and how to construct it.

The distinction between electric and magnetic field

For listening you have to choose between two types of receivers: electric field and magnetic field receivers. You just need to decide if you want to receive the magnetic or the electric component of the radio natural signal. Theoretically, the differences are small, since the two components bring the same information. In fact this double receiving option is also present in portable broadcast receivers. A VHF FM signal is received with a whip antenna (electric component), while the long and medium waves are detected with a ferrite cored internal coil, in other words a small loop (magnetic component).

The principal difference between the two techniques is the radiation pattern. The loop is bi-directional, while the whip receives equally from all directions. The suggestion that it is best to use the electric field antenna is really because this one is easier to construct than the magnetic one. The electric field receiver only needs a whip as the antenna, while the magnetic one needs a multiple turn coil or loop, and this makes it more complex, both for transporting the antenna and for mechanical construction.

How does an electric field receiver work?

As I said at the beginning of the book, an electric field receiver is not like the classic receiver we are used to, since it is wide band and without frequency conversion, so it has no tuning control. With audio band natural radio signals it is not possible to tune to a single part of the spectrum, we just listen to it all together. There just is an amplification control to adjust the signal received by the antenna to the preamplifier sensitivity, like a volume control. Because of this, receivers like these are very simple to construct and to use, because they are basically a low noise audio amplifier with high input impedance.

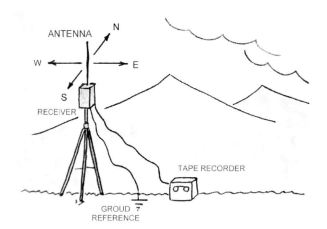

VLF receiver connection scheme: a vertical whip receives signals from all directions, with reference to the local ground.

The whip antenna, because of its small dimensions (compared to the wave length we are talking about), works as a capacitance and so the signal is received from a very high impedance, several million ohms. The best way to transfer the signal received by the antenna is to connect it to a preamplifier of the same (high) input impedance. This is what we do. Usually the input stage uses a FET (a very high impedance transistor) with several megohm input biasing resistance.

This stage has a double function, both to amplify the signal and to convert the impedance from the millions of ohms at the antenna, to few thousand ohms, more suitable for the following amplification circuits. Now the receiver front-end is complete, we need to have one or more amplification stages, depending on the connection of the receiver to the preamplifier or PC soundcard. This can be via a microphone input (preferably), to a "line" input (less sensitive because it needs a higher level signal) or directly to headphones (in which case we need much more amplification). Basically we can consider our receiver as a test-meter reading voltage between air and ground, but absorbing the least possible current so as not to disturb the field.

A simple circuit for an electric field receiver

We suggest two electric field receiver circuits which are very popular with VLF enthusiasts. Since we are talking about audio frequency circuits, construction is not difficult, and they can be created temporarily, without any soldering, on prototyping boards called "breadboards", without compromising the results. Afterwards, the working circuit can be more permanently constructed on a stripboard.

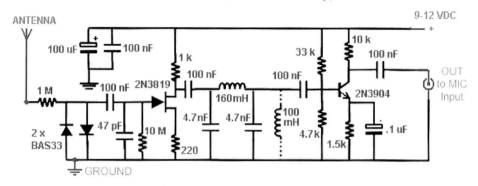

VLF BBB-4 (Steve McGreevy)

BBB4 receiver schematic. The circuit is simple but its performance is excellent. The receiver needs a good ground connection, and the output can be connected to a MIC input of a PC or a tape recorder.

The first circuit suggested is a receiver, called BBB4 and designed by Steve McGreeve, a researcher who has studied natural radio for many years.

Let us see briefly how it works. The antenna is connected through a 1 megohm resistance (which limits discharge current through the diodes), then to a pair of diodes with opposite polarity and to a coupling capacitance. This part of the circuit protects the first FET from large electric discharges and avoids the components burning-out at the first storm. At the same time it filters undesirable radio frequency signals and eliminates the DC component. The signal is then fed to the FET, which works both as amplifier and as impedance converter, going from 10 megohms at the input to around 1kilohm output impedance.

We have then a pi-section filter, constructed with an inductance and two capacitors to cut all signals higher than the audio frequency band. This avoids the amplification of medium and short-wave signals at the following stage, which would then produce intermodulation, which we discussed earlier, in the recorder or PC soundcard. The last stage is a transistor in common emitter configuration, simply for some more signal amplification.

The output signal from BBB4 is a few milliwatts and at relatively high impedance. It is not suitable to drive headphones directly, as they require more power at a lower impedance. In this case, if we want to listen to the reception live, we would have to connect the receiver to the recorder input (or PC microphone input) and to listen through the monitor. The second choice could be to use a small purpose-built amplifier, able to give the necessary power to drive the headphones or small loudspeaker.

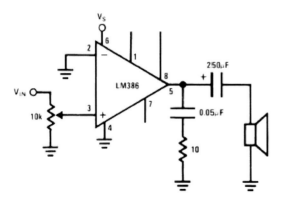

A single integrated circuit such as an LM386 can work as a preamplifier for headphones or loudspeaker. It is commonly used in portable transistor radios (schematic reproduced from National LM386 data sheets)

The circuit needs no more explanation, given that LM386 already has inside it all the components needed to make a good audio amplifier. The external components just need to power the integrated circuit and apply some filtering.

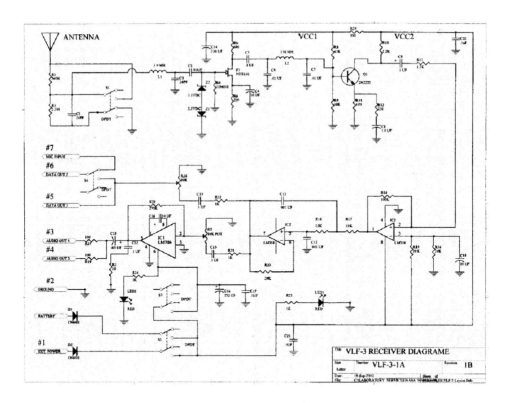

Circuit for the latest VLF receiver, designed by NASA for VLF listening. It is basically similar to BBB4, but more complete, and slightly more complex. A detailed circuit, component list and instructions for assembly are available on the NASA-Inspire web site.

If you can handle a soldering iron, the VLF-3 scheme allows a more complete project for construction. It is a receiver designed by the Inspire NASA group (we will see more about this group in a following chapter, which explains its activities) and it adds some functions to the simpler BBB-4.

The receiver is the evolution of the more popular RS-4 also designed by the same group, but with some technical improvements added. The difference between the Inspire receiver and BBB-4 is just that a high pass filter uses two operational amplifiers which reduce the disturbing noises due to the mains by reducing the receiver response below a frequency of 1000Hz. This kind of receiver differs from BBB-4 by having recording and headphone outputs. Under similar listening conditions VLF-3 and BBB-4 are very comparable and basically with the two of them we can listen to the same signals.

Antennas for electric field receivers

Whip orientation or the shape of the antenna does not directly affect reception. The receiver will always see the voltage variation, which is between a hypothetical medium antenna point and the ground reference. We will receive, the same signals by using a 2 metre whip as an antenna, or an umbrella metal frame, or even an aluminium ladder. The only elements determining the reception sensitivity are the height above the ground and the capacitance between the antenna and the ground, which depends upon the antenna surface area.

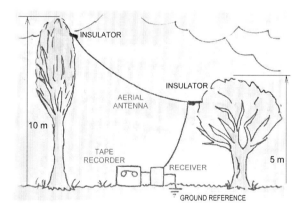

Two trees, used as a support for a VLF wire antenna. This antenna can be connected directly to a receiver such as BBB4 or VLF3.

The two receivers described are sensitive enough to work with a one metre long whip, as for instance an ordinary CB telescopic antenna. If the dimensions decrease, the sensitivity decreases as well, if they increase, we will get more signal. We can also connect a long wire antenna to the receiver, but in this case you will have to evaluate the possibility of intermodulation. If this is a problem, you will have to shorten the antenna or attenuate the signal with resistor of a few megohms placed in series with the antenna. Usually a wire antenna will be better at rejecting hum noise than a whip and is better and more sensitive for reception. This is a good reason to experiment, even if this takes few hours.

A good way to construct a vertical antenna of large dimensions but yet transportable is with fishing canes. You can buy fiberglass canes (without the reel) for a few dollars, up to eight meters long. You simply use the cane as a support for a copper wire, which becomes a high performance vertical long wire antenna.

Receiver galvanic isolation and ground reference

The receiver works by detecting the voltage variations between the antenna and the ground. It is necessary then for the receiver to have a reference ground connection. It is not necessary for it to be a very good contact (low resistance) in the electricians sense of the word. It just has to work as a "counter-balance" for the very high impedance stage, so that even a twenty centimeter stake - a tent peg or a corkscrew dog-lead fixing - inserted in the ground (damp if possible) works as an adequate ground reference. When we walk with the receiver in our hand, it is our body that becomes the reference ground, receiving the voltage difference between the whip and our body.

The antenna, especially if short, must be connected directly to the receiver without any connecting wires, certainly not coaxial feeder, for as we saw, at these frequencies, a whip acts as just a few picoFarad capacitance. Even the capacitance between the central conductor and the braid of a few meters of coaxial cable would short-circuit the signal and make the receiver very "deaf".

Sometimes when connecting the receiver to the recorder or to a portable PC, the reception suddenly becomes very noisy. This can be caused by noises radiated by the PC which arrive at the receiver through the audio connecting wires, and so they are interpreted as signals. Electrically, the ground should be the same for the two devices, but in some cases the two separate ground connections, one in the antenna and the other one on the recorder, will avoid these noises.

It is very useful, though, to remember that whatever ground connection is used, it is essential to interrupt the listening session if a storm occurs, for our safety and for the safety of the electronic devices. If possible the two devices, receiver and recorder, should be located a few meters apart, but this distance is not critical.

If, despite all this, noises are still present, then it is necessary to galvanically isolate the receiver from the recording system. This means that between the two devices there must be no metallic continuity. A simple way to achieve this function is to use transformers.

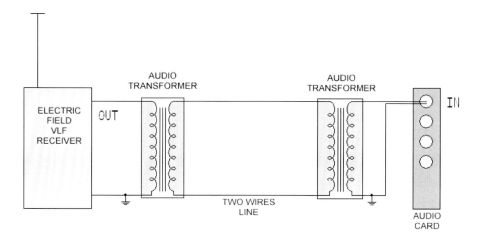

A simple way to create a galvanic insulation. This way, noises created by PC, are isolated from the receiver.

You can easily use the audio transformers from the final MOSFET stage of an audio amplifier. These usually are of very good quality, with high performance in the audio band. They do have a downside; they are rather expensive and you cannot find them everywhere. Apart from them you can use a small toroidal transformer as are used in the power supplies. They have a very good bandwidth from few hertz to dozens of kilohertz and you can recover them from old power supplies or other obsolete devices.

The floating receiver

A variant to the electric field receiver is the floating receiver. The signal now is not taken between a "hot" terminal, the whip antenna, and the ground plane, but between two symmetrical "hot" terminals, both separated from the receiver ground. This way, you can isolate receiver from the listening station, without using transformers.

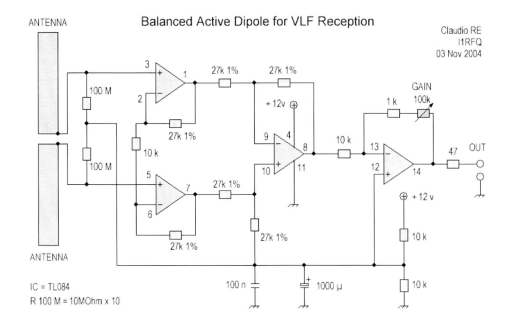

Balanced Active Dipole for VLF Reception

Claudio RE
I1RFQ
03 Nov 2004

IC = TL084
R 100 M = 10MOhm x 10

A single integrated circuit (TL084) with some resistances can be used to construct this simple but efficient receiver.

The floating receiver has a very high input impedance and it can work with a very small antenna. The smallest model you can build consists of two metallic cylinders mounted axially. It can even be simply two aluminium sheets wrapped around a plastic tube as a support. The requirement is that they must be very well isolated one from the other.

Tube and cylinder dimensions are not critical: the antenna is not resonant, so you do not have to tune it. The power, in this case, is supplied by a solar panel, and a sealed lead-acid storage battery allows its use at night time.

The main advantage of the floating receiver is in avoiding using the ground reference and so being totally independent from it. This has two advantages, first the receiver does not receive noises coming from the ground connection, but it collects the signal present in the air only, and secondly it does not receive noises from the PC via the connecting cables to spoil reception.

Here an example of a floating receiver maintained with a small solar panel. The mast is wooden, while the tube is made of plastic waste-pipe 1 meter long, on which two aluminium sheets are wrapped. The two cylinders work as an air capacitance and they work by detecting the voltage difference between them.

The magnetic field receiver

The magnetic field receiver is certainly more critical and laborious to construct, even if some of its characteristics make it more suitable for radio direction-finding functions. The magnetic field antenna (loop) is directional, and it functions in a very similar way to the ferrite antenna inside a medium wave AM portable receiver. If we want to get a stronger signal then we change the orientation of the ferrite-rod antenna, by rotating the receiver itself.

If we use two antennas placed at 90° to each other, this characteristic allows us to determine the direction of an incoming signal without moving the antennas. We will see in a following chapter how the FFT aids our work, particularly for radio direction-finding, and how this facility uses the two loop antennas placed at 90° from each other.

The loop permits us to exclude signals coming from one direction. This can be, sometimes be used to reduce interference created by the electrical system buzzing. Changing the loop direction, to avoid hum noises, works only partially for two reasons.

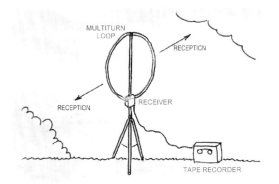

The loop, unlike the whip antenna, does not need a ground connection to work. Its radiation diagram is different; it has a null, perpendicular to the coil plane. This characteristic can be useful for excluding a troublesome signal from reception.

The first one is that hum noise usually comes from several directions, not just one. Also, when nulling the 50(60)Hz values, we can still have very large signals at 150(180), 250(300), and 350(420)Hz and vice-versa. The second reason is that the loop inductively couples, not only with the signals to be received, but also with near field signals (magnetic component) induced by the electric mains network. The electric field receiver is totally deaf to these signals.

In effect, the loop becomes the secondary winding of a giant transformer; where the core is the air and the primary winding is made up of the electricity lines, which run for kilometers around the listening station. The loop does not need a ground reference and so it is immune to noises coming from the receiver (through the wire), which can otherwise happen in the case of the ground referenced electric field receiver. Despite this, using loop rather than whip can easily bring problems.

The magnetic field receiver is also a simple audio frequency amplifier, but, unlike the electric field receiver which must operate with a very high impedance signal, it has to amplify a very low impedance signal, of a few ohms.

Magnetic field receiver, simple projects

While for the electric field receiver the ideal input circuit is of theoretically infinite impedance, for the loop the amplifier should theoretically have zero impedance. A closed loop, from where the current is taken off without any drop in voltage, represents the opposite of a whip in which the voltage is read without taking any current.

In this case we have two solutions to match to the impedance. The first one is the use of an impedance transformer to connect between the antenna (loop) and the receiver (the amplifier). This performs a step-up from the value of few ohms, present in the loop output, to a few kilohms so that we can transfer the energy captured by the antenna to the amplifier as a voltage.

The amplifier does not work in a linear way, its amplification decreases as the frequency gets higher, due to an integrator circuit. This non-linear amplification compensates for the small dimension loops, which receive more signal at high frequencies than at lower frequencies. This allows us to have a linear frequency response at the output of the amplifier, as we had for the electric field receiver.

The most critical part to find is the impedance transformer. We can use the audio transformers, that were used between audio amplifier valve and loudspeaker in the 1950s, with good results. They are not easy to find though, and they are rather expensive. A good alternative is to buy transformers for modern audio amplifiers, but paying the right prices. The final alternative is, like the galvanic isolation used in the electric field receivers, the toroidal transformers used in power supplies.

It is very important to choose models with a high primary to secondary ratio, since because the impedance transforming factor is the square of the turns ratio. A 220v to 11v step-down transformer has an impedance ratio of 20 x 20 = 400 times. If we are using it with a 5 ohm loop we will have a 2000 ohm output impedance, which is adequate for feeding to a normal audio amplifier.

An alternative solution, used recently, employs an operational amplifier circuit which creates a virtual short-circuit at the input. This permits us to work at very low impedance without using transformers.

Using a circuit like this, we can avoid the problems of the transformer, and we can obtain the same results as those obtained with a traditional system. The two operational amplifier pins, connected to the loop, are maintained by the circuit itself at the same electric potential; this way the loop antenna "sees" a short-circuit, even if virtual, and transfers, without loss, all the captured energy as current.

A single operational amplifier works both as an impedance converter and amplifier, whose output can be directly connected either to the input line of the recorder, or to the line input of a portable PC. This kind of circuit does not need the integrator correction. Working with current, the output is linear with frequency, this means that signals of the same intensity induce in the loop the same currents whatever the frequency.

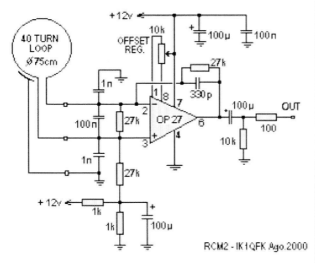

The simple EasyLoop circuits (RCM2) using a single operational amplifier.

The trimmer controls the input offset only and must be tuned to have 6V DC on pin 6. No other adjustments are required. Turn on the receiver and it works immediately, amplifying the signals coming from the loop.

A prototype of the loop. As support, a plastic hoola-hoop ring has been used. It has been cut on the external edge, and the wire stuffed inside.

The voltage present at the ends of a loop, placed in a known field, can be calculated as follows.

$$E[V] = 7.89 \times 10^{-6} \times N[turns] \times A\ [m^2] \times F[Hz] \times H[A/m]$$

N is the number of turns, A is the area of to loop, F is the frequency and H is the magnetic field intensity.

Antennas for magnetic field reception

The construction of a loop antenna for audio band reception does not present many difficulties. It is basically just a big coil built in the air, the conductors provide the signal directly. Some problems come from mechanical matters: the total loop surface (the area of a single turn multiplied by the number of turns), must be at least a dozen square meters. Also the coil must not be made very small, otherwise it will need many turns to achieve the area, and, at that point, the parasitic capacitance between separate turns spoils its operation at the higher frequencies.

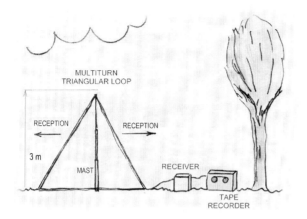

A quick magnetic field loop, built in few minutes. It takes only a mast support and some meters of electrical wire.

This simple but a big antenna gives much more sensitivity than a small portable loop, because the antenna sensitivity is proportional to the loop area.

A good compromise in dimensions for loop design is from 60 centimetres to 1 metre diameter. A 60cm loop has a 0.28 square meters area, needing at least 35 turns to get to the needed surface area, while a 1 metre diameter loop has a 0.78 square meters surface, needing at least 13 turns to work in a similar way.

The antenna receives signals in the direction of the plane of the coil, and has its null on the axis of the coil. The loop must be maintained in vertical position, to receive signals in that polarization. A VLF signal propagates by ground waves, which have vertical polarization. If we put the loop in horizontal position we will not receive any natural signals, but we can hear a very high hum noise, because the loop inductively couples to the main electrical power lines, which are themselves in horizontal position.

The support around which the coil is wrapped can be made of plastic or wood, but it can also be metallic (such as for instance a bicycle wheel). In that case you need to interrupt the metal for a few centimeters, because a closed circle would represent a single turn with a short-circuit which would absorb all the received signal. The loop shielding effect on reception quality at these frequencies is negligible. But it is however useful to protect the amplifier circuit from static fields which could damage it. The antenna does not have to be tuned for this application because it is not used as resonant antenna, but as a broadband sensor.

The coil shape itself is not that important. A circular loop will optimize the relationship between wire length and obtained surface area, but an octagonal or square shape work just as well. It is sensible for us to use the shape that is easiest to construct. During out-door sessions we can use a triangular loop constructed on support a few meters high, and with its base on the ground (the height of a loop antenna from the ground has no effect on its sensitivity to signals) a 4 metres base, 2 metres high with 5 turns is an antenna with very good sensitivity.

The wire used must be a diameter of at least half millimeter. Because a smaller cross-section will increase the coil resistance, degrading the antenna performance at low frequencies. Usually telephone twisted-pair, or the cable used for intercom phones, is a good operational compromise. If you can find a multi-conductor wire you can construct a multi-turn loop by just building a single coil, and connecting the conductors in series to obtain the required number of turns to make the system work properly.

Converting units of measurement

These start to bother us even as little children, because there are equivalences and conversions between different measurement units. In such a complex field as that of radio signals, there are many ways of expressing them. Converting between one and the other can sometimes complicate our life and make some simple calculations very tedious. They are the classical banana skin, which can trip up even the most prepared mind.

The following table is simple and easy to consult:

Starting from	Doing:			
MAGNETIC FIELD H In ampere/meter **(A/m)**	-	Multiplied 375	Divided 0.8	Divided 8
ELECTRIC FIELD E In volt/meter **(V/m)**	Divided 375	-	Divided 300	Divided 3000
MAGNETIC INDUCTION B In microtesla **(µT)**	Multiplied 0.8	Multiplied 300	-	Divided 10
MAGNETIC INDUCTION In milligauss **(mG)**	Multiplied 8	Multiplied 3000	Multiplied 10	-
	We obtain:			
	A/m	V/m	µT	mG

For example, if you want to know whether a loop with a certain dimension is able to receive a certain signal or not, you find this problem. The signal we want to receive is known in pT (picoTesla), but the formula allowing us to calculate the voltage present at the end of the loop requires a field expressed in A/m.

When we talk about measurement at VLF, we talk about electric field, magnetic field and magnetic induction. They all express the intensity of a signal but they do it through different parameters. The electric field is generated by electric charges and indicates the perturbation of a space in which they are the working forces. The magnetic field indicates a space where magnetic dipoles are reduced to a couple of forces orientating them. The magnetic induction indicates the intensity of the magnetic flux per square centimeter.

If, for example, we know the value of a signal expressed in μT and we want to know what is its value in A/m, to calculate the voltage present at the ends of a loop, we just have to multiply the known value by 0.8.

8. Recording VLF signals

Once the first rush of enthusiasm for these new, weird, and fascinating signals has passed, when we are just happy to wander in the country with our receiver in our hand and the headphones on, we feel we must to collect and file the data, in order to analyze and study it. Perhaps also, we would like to compare them with the ones received by other stations.

Tape recording

Until recently, a tape recorders was, without doubt, the most readily available system, the cheapest and most comfortable one. A portable tape recorder, some compact cassettes and the recording activity can begin. We must, however, understand some of the limits of this system, which could affect the quality of the data we save.

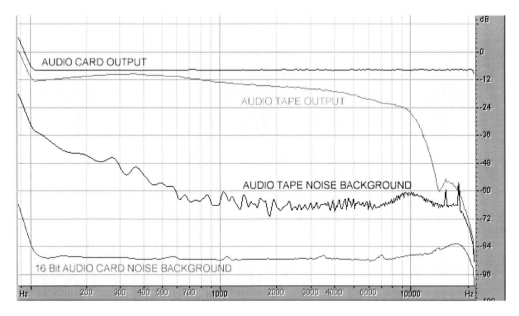

The pass-band and available dynamic range of an audio tape, compared to the audio card. Although a high quality chrome tape has been used, the final performance is poor compared to a basic and cheap PC soundcard.

The first limitation is the available audio bandwidth. A portable recorder, usually works with ferrous tapes in a frequency range from 100Hz to 11kHz (even

74

if in the instruction manual it says from 20 Hz to 20 kHz), the performance gets better by using "chrome" or "metal" tapes, but portable recorders will not always support these tape options.

The stored recordings will disappear with time, or at least will grow weaker. This is more difficult to recognize with modern pop music than with classical music, but a few years after the recording, where the recording level was very low (for instance in a violin piece) the instrumental sound could have disappeared. In the same way you can record a hissing wave and if it is submerged in statics, after few years you are not able to find it, all you will find are the statics.

The dynamic range of a tape is rather limited. There are effectively 40 decibels (dB) available but not over the whole band. This means that if the maximum volume reached by a signal is 100mV, the minimum detectable recorded signal will be 1mV, while lower level signals will be swamped by the tape noise. Basically we could listen to a weak signal, record it, and then later just hear background noise only, on the recorded tape.

The last problem comes from automatic volume (or level) control systems (ALC). Almost every portable recorder has them and usually, we cannot disable this function. It is generally intended to help the internal microphone to catch a voice no matter how far from the recorder the speaker is. However with impulsive signals, such as the statics, the ALC starts to lower and pump up the volume making the recording unusable. Where it is not possible turn off this function, you must adjust the signal input, to make sure it is below the activation level of the ALC.

DAT recordings

For some years DAT (Digital Audio Tape) was the only valid alternative to technically sophisticated professional analogue portable recorders. They are digital data recorders, with an analogue to digital converter (ADC) at the input and a digital to analogue converter (DAC) for playback. The recording is digital (just two levels representing numbers that describe the level), and so it is not subject to the degradation we described in the analogue recorder. Also, they have a wide bandwidth (from 10Hz to 22kHz) and most importantly they have a very high dynamic range, similar to a Compact Disc (CD). In simple terms, if a 100mV signal represents the maximum volume acceptable, the DAT is able to capture signals down to 0.032mV (a big difference from the 1mV of the magnetic tape).

Some models allow the use of data compression increasing the recording time with the same tape. It is important to remember that this function is destructive (while the computer ZIP file will leave the original content intact) and, as we will see in the following paragraph, which describes MP3 players, it is not useful for our kind of activity.

MP3 recordings

Players/recorders for MP3 format have become very popular nowadays, mainly for Internet music download. MP3 is a compression algorithm, and is a destructive one. The vocal file is analyzed into its component parts the least important are removed, so it becomes shorter. The choice of the sound components to be cut out is based on psychology and is done, for instance on a modern music piece, in such a way that we do not notice these cuts. This system is hated by classical music experts because the algorithm makes entire instrumentals "disappear" when the sound is very weak, because they are tagged as noise. If we think about natural origin radio signals which are very similar to noises themselves, we can see that these devices are not suitable for VLF signal recordings. Their effect on weak signals is sometimes devastating.

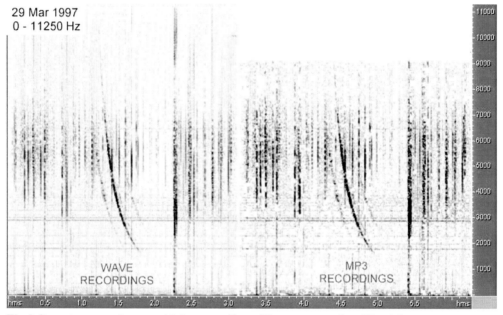

The left spectrogram shows a whistler recording without compression. The right part presents the same one compressed with the MP3 algorithm. Note how frequencies over 9kHz are deleted and below this limit the spectrogram appears full of white holes.

PCM recordings: the audio card

The spread and popularity of the portable PC made this kind of activity possible and easy, through the use of the soundcard. The audio (or sound) card can record audio signals digitally with a very good dynamic range of up to 90dB, and a wide bandwidth from few Hz to 22kHz. While the card is recording, or better "acquiring", it is possible to follow the input signal graphically and we are then able to move the receiver to optimize its performance, whilst seeing a real-time spectrogram of the captured signal.

For a comparison, let us think about the old and very expensive tape recorders that were used in disc recording studios to make vinyl masters, they allowed the signals to be recorded up to 19kHz with a maximum dynamic range of 60dB. Nowadays all commercially available audio cards perform the sampling at 44,000 readings per second (a value called the Sampling Rate) allowing for a 22kHz bandwidth, and with up to 16 bit resolution (the bit number is the number of binary digits used to define the signal amplitude), giving a total dynamic range of 90dB.

A cheap PCI audio card: 24.00 Euro at a computer shop, or 8.00 Euro on eBay.

For used in natural radio recording we do not need sophisticated digital signal processing or special effects, a low noise input such as the "line" is enough.

The audio card is a very important part because even if the signal is first acquired by tape recording, we have to transpose it into a wave file, with a signal digitizing device, to obtain a signal analysis.

In some portable PCs the audio card performance is not very good, particularly if they are built-in on the PC motherboard. The low frequency performance is poor, it does not go below 40Hz, they are noisy (because of the local noise coupled from the digital circuits nearby, and inadequate shielding), they will easily go into cross-modulation and the input levels are not always fully controllable with the Windows mixer.

The size of a cigarette pack: this is a USB audio card, to be preferred to one built into a portable PC. Starting from 50 Euro.

9. Analysis software

To listen to, and record, a signal without creating a spectrogram of it, is like being in front of a landscape and just hearing the description of it, instead of looking at it. The spectrogram is a full graphical representation of a signal, which gives us an image describing the specific characteristics which make it a unique item, like a digital fingerprint. Before the advent of the PC, this system was used by only a few dozen institutes in the whole world, and the equipment to do it was big, slow and so expensive, that it would have cost as much as a luxury car.

Then, first Apple Macintosh software came out. The most popular was *SoundEdit* from MacroMedia during the 1980s, and it was the first readily accessible system for private use, even if not inexpensive. Finally, the rapid advance of technology, made it possible to perform every kind of analysis we could want to make on an audio signal, on anyone's PC.

The following two programs are a good approach to learning how to use FFT analysis. They give access to the principle commands only, excluding the possibility of handling other parameters. This characteristic limits the performance from one point of view, but avoids erroneous settings, so is more usable by non-experts. We will consider higher performance software later.

Spectrogram

The first one to make available this function in Windows was an American: Richard Horne, with his popular *Spectrogram*. This application can be downloaded from his site (http://www.visualizationsoftware.com), but copies of this software are everywhere on many software archive lists. Versions from 6.0 are shareware, while earlier ones are free. The program permits analysis of the input signals to the audio card in real time, allows recordings to be made in wave format, and also allows analysis of wave files in stereo.

There are a few essential commands available listed below with the meanings of the most important ones.

Sample rate establishes how many times per second the sampler reads the input signal, and therefore the highest frequency (equal to the half of the sample rate). So a 22kS/s sample rate determines an 11kHz high frequency limit.

In Resolution, the number of bits determines the recording dynamics, because with 8 bit we have 45dB (like an old audio tape), while with 16 bit we have 90dB (and a double disc file size).

The dB scale determines how much of the 90dB is to be shown on the spectrogram.

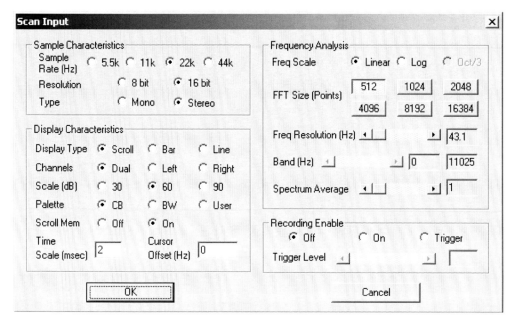

The simple *Spectrogram* menu.

"Time Scale" establishes in ms the time between one spectrogram display line and the next. A low value, such as 20ms makes the spectrogram run quickly, while higher value, such as 2000ms, will make it run more slowly.

The "FFT size" determines the number of calculated points to make a spectrogram. If we set it up with many points (16384) we will have a higher frequency resolution, but the definition in the time decreases and the frequency band displayed is narrower. If fewer points (512) are selected, we will have a lower frequency resolution but the spectrogram can display faster signals and the frequency range displayed is bigger.

Talking practically, selecting a sample rate of 44kHz and 512 points, we will see a 22kHz frequency range. If we increase to 16384 points, the frequency range displayed becomes 689Hz. We have a 689Hz wide window to position anywhere we want in the 1 to 22kHz range.

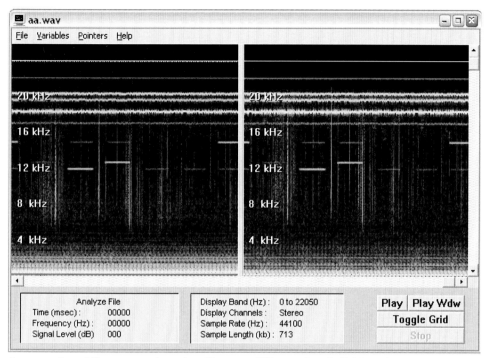

Analyze File		Display Band (Hz):	0 to 22050		Play	Play Wdw
Time (msec):	00000	Display Channels:	Stereo			
Frequency (Hz):	00000	Sample Rate (Hz):	44100		Toggle Grid	
Signal Level (dB)	000	Sample Length (kb):	713		Stop	

A screen shot of *Spectrogram* in action. Here two different electric field receivers' performance is compared, from 0 to 22kHz. The two signals sound almost the same to our ear, but the spectrogram analysis shows some differences.

Spectran

One interesting free program is of Italian origin and is called *Spectran*. It was written by two Italian radio amateurs: Alberto Di Bene, I2PHD, and Vittorio De Tomasi, IK2CZL. The software was first conceived to be used in the study of signals coming from a standard amateur radio receiver, but it is perfectly adaptable to VLF band signal study. Particular care was given to the user interface to make the program easy use. The program is downloadable from the author's website: http://www.weaksignals.com. Or, as for *Spectrogram*, from the main on-line software data-bases. Here is a description of the use of the main commands.

In the control window you can choose, as for *Spectrogram*, the sampling rate. The authors have determined the choice of the number of FFT point calculated in terms of the frequency resolution arising from it. The result is a "resolution" button which has the same function as for the buttons with the point numbers in the Horne program. The spectrogram running speed is adjustable from the main window together with the "slider" controls adjusting brightness, and contrast. Another slide control directly adjusts the spectrogram speed.

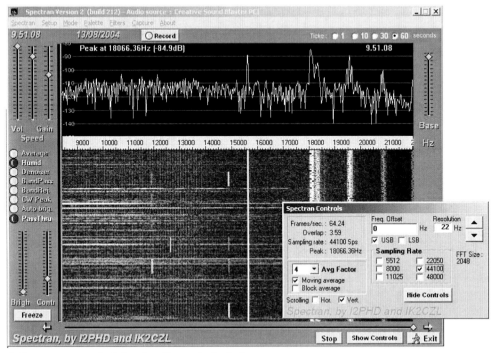

A *Spectran* screenshot showing the control window.

If we compare *Spectran* to *Spectrogram*, the former allows a better frequency resolution and it incorporates a filter called "Humid" which in real time removes the hum noise in a miraculous way. The performance is very useful if we do long listening sessions in busy places. Having to listen to two hours of buzzing, whilst looking for a weak but interesting signal is not an ideal situation. If the listening session is in a place such as a garden or a field close to our house, this kind of filter becomes very useful and very valuable.

The program has recording and wave file reading facilities, and permits automatic saving of the window image, so allowing the automatic building of a visual documentation of all the analyzed signals. This software, unlike *Spectrogram*, works only on a single channel, and not on the stereo pair.

10. Coordinated listening

One of the most interesting activities we can experiment with in monitoring and the study of natural radio is coordinated listening, where different listeners in different places make simultaneous recordings. When the collected signals are compared between them in this way, it is possible to study the signal characteristics and to determine whether some signals have a local or a wide area character. The first VLF coordinated listening sessions happened during an American NASA project called INSPIRE, which we will now consider in more detail.

The INSPIRE project

After few minor experiments called HSGS/ACTIVE - a Moscow Space institute initiative, when a Russian satellite with a 10.5kHz transmitter on board was monitored at hundreds of sites on the Earth in 1992 - the INSPIRE (Interactive NASA Space Physics Ionosphere Radio Experiments) project was born.

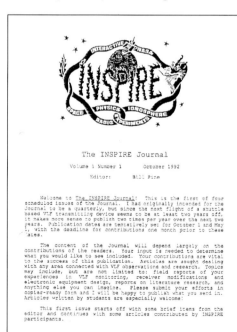

In October 1992 the first issue of the *INSPIRE Journal* was published, where experiments in March of the same year were documented. The Russian project involved 100 sites, whereas INSPIRE involved over 1000 schools, and technical institutes just in the America.

The experiment consisted of the emission of VLF band signals from Space and consequent wide-spread monitoring of these signals. The transmissions were made from the Space Shuttle and were part of a research project called SEPAC (Space Experiments with Particle Accelerators).

The cover of the first *INSPIRE Journal*, October 1992.

The Space Shuttle did not have a real physical antenna to transmit on such low frequencies, but it used a virtual one, using the electron flux emitted by a particle gun. The 6.2kW powered electronic gun injected tones of different frequencies into the ionosphere, starting from 7050Hz and going down to 50Hz.

The modulated electron stream from the gun generated an electromagnetic field. It was believed that the propagation of this field could have occurred along the magnetic field lines, due to the ionization gradient and so they would propagate as if they were inside a wave-guide. The electron flux should have arrived at the Earth's surface more or less as it happens inside a cathode ray tube, following the magnetic field path, like whistlers.

The objective was to determinate the signal coverage area, the path attenuation, and possibly any unconventional paths followed. A plasma generator on the Shuttle attempted a transmission by plasma emission into Space. The target of this study was to determinate the transparency of the ionosphere to VLF signals and the efficiency of a non-conventional signal transmission system, which might be able to be used during a spaceship's re-entry, during the radio black-out period.

NASA involved several American high schools in this study, designing a simple-to-build VLF receiver (similar to the one described earlier) and also extended the possibility of cooperation to US radio amateurs. This was a way of getting country-wide coverage without incurring high costs. The idea of collaborating with NASA was exciting for a lot of people, and within a few years, this was extended to cover the whole world, not just America.

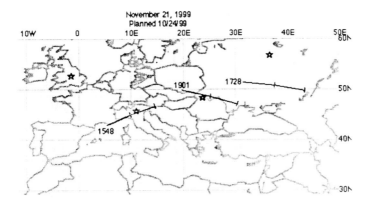

21 November 1999: map of Europe with MIR passing and its relative times

Transmission times were programmed in advance so that the different Earth crews could organize observing sessions at electromagnetically quiet sites. The recorded tapes (for which there was a very strict protocol about how to do the recordings) were sent to Bill Pine, NASA project coordinator, who analyzed them and who made spectrograms, publishing the results in the next *INSPIRE Journal*.

A picture of the MIR station. Source: http://www.globalgeografia.com/

This kind of experiment, begun on the Shuttle, was then transferred to the orbiting Russian space-station MIR in 1995, and became a regular event every spring and fall for the group of keen researchers. For many orbits, MIR passed over our heads transmitting its signal at frequencies of 10Hz and 1kHz, using a plasma generator called ARIEL and electronic gun called ISTOCHNIK. The last VLF MIR transmission was in November 1999, and the following Spring the space station was abandoned, finally burning up on re-entry and falling into the ocean.

The most strange aspect of all this activity is that during eight years experimentation, no listener on Earth ever received these VLF emissions. Perhaps the power used was not enough to overcome the path attenuation. Or perhaps, the signals arrived on Earth but they were swamped by natural noises. A few years later after the cessation of the MIR tests, INSPIRE management mentioned possible future, more powerful transmissions, directly from the International

Space Station (ISS). However the delays in construction due to international economic problems, means we cannot expect further VLF projects in the near future. The INSPIRE Group is still active but its activity is concentrated on natural origin radio signal listening.

Time coordinated listening

Technically, INSPIRE, failed its objective, or rather it established that the VLF signal does not reach the Earth (this can be consider "a result"). Educationally, INSPIRE had a great effect by spreading knowledge of this kind of research in those narrow boundaries between amateur radio activity and scientific experimentation.

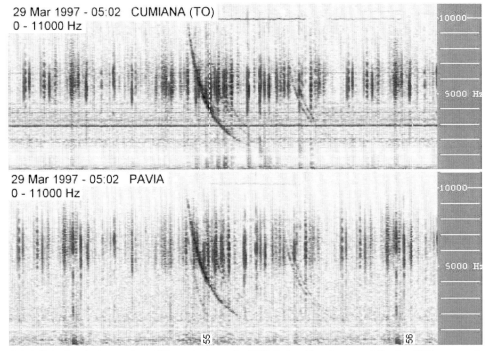

Joint listening between two different places in NW Italy: Cumiana and Pavia, 100km apart. The two recording are very similar. Recordings by Renato Romero and Ezio Mognaschi.

As well as listening for the emissions coming from the space, listening sessions at sunrise, which was the most propitious moment to capture natural radio signals, were organized. The objective here was to compare the difference in reception on Earth from site to site. It was in these conditions that, for instance, it was discovered that statics do not propagate for just a thousand kilometers as we had thought, but the signal generated by lightning can reach two points up to 7.000 kilometres apart.

Those days also saw the birth of the website http://www.vlf.it which was first envisaged to make VLF documentation available. Then it changed and became an on-line "openlab" research laboratory, thanks to numerous collaborations. Nowadays this site, from which this book originated, is one of the biggest worldwide private resources on VLF, and researchers from all over the world use it to collaborate.

Time references

One of the main problems to solve since the beginning of the idea of coordinated listening was that of "time references". We need to be able to compare a half a second of hissing wave reception, received by two different operators using different receivers to listen and to record, and then to be sure both are dealing with the same signal. This is not a trivial thing! A couple of seconds uncertainty between the sites, can make the comparisons very difficult, or even impossible.

The most popular synchronization system is to record, at the beginning of the tape, a voice announcement with date and recording time of the session. Next the time signal from a broadcast station is recorded in real time (on the hour or every half hour), and without stopping the tape we then switch on the VLF receiver. Every ten minutes, always without stopping the tape, we record a Beep at the end of the tenth minute. If broadcast signals are not available, you can use a good watch, synchronized the same day.

This way we can be certain of the beginning time and end time when we come to the analysis. We will have time references to correct any speed variation in the recorders. Not all recorders run at the same speed, or even at a stable speed, due to the tolerances inherent in a low-cost mass-produced product. It can happen that a 60 minute tape lasts only 58 minutes on one recorder and 63 minutes on another. Then the researcher, who receives five different tapes to analyze and to compare, really has a hard time.

If the listening sessions are in wintertime we need to acclimatize the recorder at the ambient temperature. If the recorder is taken from home at 20°C and taken into a field at 0°C, its speed will vary depending on the drive belt and pulley temperature. This complication grows during analysis time: If the speed in not correct in absolute terms, and it is not constant, we cannot align the recordings or spectrograms in time, so we cannot be sure we are looking at the same event at both sites.

If we use a portable PC this becomes much easier: It is sufficient to synchronize the PC clock, though Internet. This operation can be done automatically with one of the many time programs such as *Automachron*, freely downloadable (http://oneguycoding.com) or software available from NIST in the US. You just have to insert into the program the host name (for instance time-a.nist.gov) and the protocol used (SNPTV4) in a simple form and you'll have the right time on your PC clock from the server you selected.

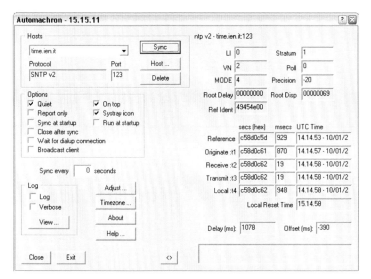

The *Automachron* window control, after a synch time operation. Some operating systems, like Windows XP, do this function automatically, in a "time and date scheduled" session.

Even Windows, from XP on, incorporates the ability to synchronize the PC clock with an external server. This function is activated with a double click on the clock key and clicking on "Internet time".

Usually portable PC quartz stability guarantees a few seconds tolerance every week, which is more than enough for our task. The date and time information in wave files make the vocal announcement of the time redundant for the audio tapes.

11. The physics of the sun

In this chapter, we will look at how VLF signal reception relates to different physical phenomena. VLF natural radio signals are linked to the activity of the sun and an understanding the basic mechanism which governs this will be a great help in receiving and interpreting the signals. We started with passive listening (where we just accepted whatever we heardd), but we can now move to an activity based on forecasting the best conditions for natural radio listening, acquired from solar activity data.

How does the sun work?

The closest star, just another way to describe the object 150 million kilometres away, is composed of hydrogen and it is what sustains life on Earth. At its centre, with a temperature of millions of degrees Celsius and with tremendous gravitational pressure, the hydrogen is transformed into helium by a nuclear fusion process. Solar activity is not perfectly regular, but is characterized by explosions (called solar flares). To make a simple homely comparison, we could say that the sun seems more similar to the fireplace activity than to a regular kitchen gas flame.

A solar explosion on an active area: loops after the flare are visible.

Image captured by TRACE spacecraft. Source: Locked Martin Advanced Technology Center, reproduced with NASA authorization.

Indications of this turbulent activity are the Sun-spots, visible on its surface, some of which can be bigger than the diameter of the Earth. Their temperature is several million degrees cooler of the rest of the surface, which is why they seem darker than the surrounding surface. The sun rotates on its axis, as the Earth does, but with a 27 day cycle and the turbulence periods linked to the Sun-spots often have this same periodicity.

Solar activity has an 11 year cycle and radio amateurs know this cycle well. During periods of minimum solar activity, with very few sun-spots, they find the best conditions to use low frequencies bands under 7MHz. Low atmospheric noise and good ionospheric reflection make these frequencies a good choice for long distance communications. On higher frequencies, with the reflection effect decreasing, radio frequency transmissions are limited to shorter ranges. During maximum solar activity years, conditions are inverted. Low frequency bands become unusable because of noise and high frequency bands have good propagation conditions. The effects of this activity are result of the solar wind and the solar flux, so let us see the difference between them.

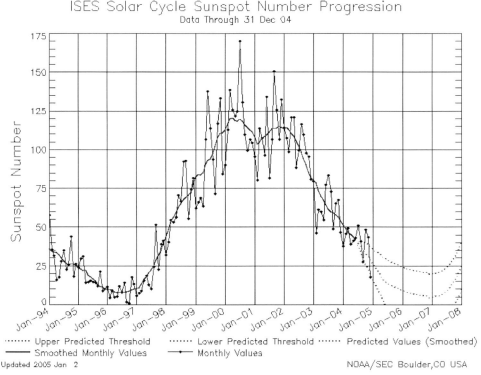

The solar cycle in the last 14 years. Source NOOA.

Solar flux

Solar flux is composed of all types of solar radiation, not only optical, infrared and ultraviolet, but also radio signals, and X-rays. Since we are simply talking about energy, these emissions propagate at the speed of light and it takes them eight minutes to make the trip from the Sun to the Earth. This means that the sunlight we see has departed eight minutes earlier. If someone were to switch the sun off we would continue to see its light for eight minutes more.

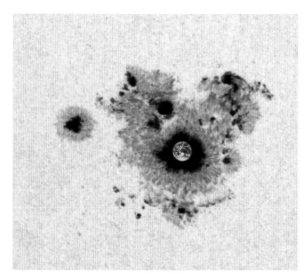

Solar flares are the result of high power explosions. The sun spots, we can sometimes see when looking at the sun's surface at sunset, are bigger than our planet.

The trick picture alongside shows, with real proportions, the Earth (photographed during Apollo 17 mission) inside a sun spot (detected by TRACE satellite).

Source: http://scijinks.jpl.nasa.gov

Reproduced with NASA authorization.

Ultraviolet and X-Rays cause most atmosphere ionization, and are responsible for good transmission on short waves. Usually their presence will worsen low-band conditions and improve higher bands. During electromagnetic storms, when large quantities of X-rays invade the ionosphere, the daylight hemisphere ionizes extensively even at low layers, degrading all transmissions for hours. This phenomenon is known as "short wave fade-out". VLF transmission may be enhanced during these events and amateur astronomers monitor VLF stations to watch for flare activity. They are recorded as SID (sudden ionospheric disturbance), observed/recorded by monitoring the SES (Sudden enhancements of signal strength) of extremely stable VLF transmissions (15 to 50kHz).

Solar activity measurement

By using the Internet we are able to know the solar flux intensity, in real time. Usually we consider two parameters. In Ottawa, Canada, they measure the solar flux coming from the sun at the 10.3 centimeter wavelength (2800MHz), the published value is proportional to the current number of sun spots. Satellites measure the X-ray flux emitted by the sun, using a five step scale, to indicate levels from "very low" to "high".

Solar wind

The solar wind is composed of electrons, protons, and helium nuclei thrown off by the sun as it rotates. Because it has mass, the solar wind travels much more slowly than solar flux, and in normal conditions it travels at about 400km/sec and it takes almost four and a half days to reach our planet.

A solar burst impacts against our ionosphere. Image created by SOHO, of Steele Hill. Reproduced with NASA authorization. Source: http://scijinks.jpl.nasa.gov

If we return to the fire metaphor, we can compare the solar flux to the heat and light developed by a fire (you can see it immediately from far away), while the solar wind can be compared to the smoke that we only can see afterwards.

When the solar wind arrives at our planet, some is captured by the terrestrial magnetic field (magnetosphere) which, being well beyond our atmosphere, impedes its arrival at the surface, trapping it in a bun-shaped region around the Earth. During magnetic storms, which can even last for days, clouds of plasma ejected by the sun at a very high speed, deform the magnetosphere and so provoke intensity variations in the terrestrial magnetic field. In these conditions the ionosphere, even as an indirect effect, does not reflect HF signals well, and the maximum frequency tends to decrease.

The solar wind is also responsible for aurora and for the canal formation. Those canals allow the birth of the whistler wave, so this is a very important parameter we should consider.

Geomagnetic activity measurement

This is the activity which, as natural radio signal amateurs, is close to us, given that it indicates the greatest likelihood of these phenomena occurring, and will allow us to listen to whistlers, hissing and chorus.

The measure of geomagnetic activity is derived from observations and it indicates how variable the terrestrial magnetic field intensity is. If the index is very high, it means that a large quantity of solar wind is striking the magnetosphere.

The most common value we can find on the Internet is the A index from Boulder (Colorado), which is quoted daily and has values from 0 (quiet) to 400 (severe storm). This index is obtained by calculating the daily average of K index, which is calculated every three hours and is represented from 0 to 9 on a logarithmic scale.

12. Natural radio signals in the sub-audio band (ELF and ULF)

This chapter begins with a dissertation about those signals we can't hear because they are out of (or below) the audio band. This means signals in the range from 1Hz to 100Hz, and too deep to be interpreted by human ear. These signals are nevertheless in both the reception window and in the working audio band of the audio cards, so they are able to be processed. Obviously, for these signals we won't talk of listening, but of visualization through spectrograms. They could actually be heard with the help of a conversion process, from deep sound up to audio frequency. However, since they changing very slowly they would also need to be accelerated in speed, and then what we would listen to would be a re-interpretation adapted to the human ear, and very far from the characteristics of the original signal.

Schumann resonances

Schumann resonances are, from many viewpoints, a classic example of this kind of signal, for two main reasons. First, because they constitute the natural background noise from 5 to 45Hz and their reception indicates that the receiving system is in good health. When listening to Schumann resonances it is receiving the weakest signal on those frequencies. The second reason is because they are strictly related to physical well-being and to several mental processes, given their concomitance with electro-encephalogram (EEG) signals. This subject will be more deeply investigated in a following chapter, about pseudo-sciences. It really is an interesting signal to receive because it is cited in many studies in some very different fields.

These signals take the name of W O Schumann, a German scientist from Munich, who foresaw their existence in 1952 as a result of a mathematical hypothesis. Their existence was scientifically verified many years later. Schumann resonances originate from the resonance formed by the cavity between Earth and its ionosphere, which is excited by statics.

The mechanism is very similar to the one when we take an empty bottle and blow over it; a "fuuu" sound is generated on the same frequency, whether we blow strongly, or gently. The frequency of the tone is a natural function of the size of the bottle (cavity). The Earth-ionosphere cavity is excited (blown) by thousands of static discharges, which happen over the whole globe, making the tone constant and continuous.

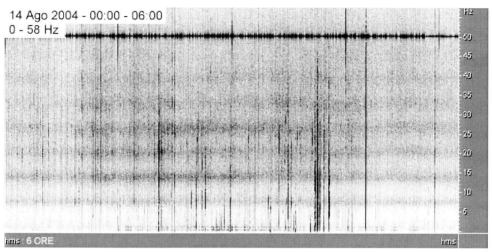

Schumann resonances, received in six hours of recording in Cumiana (NW-Italy) with a Marconi antenna. They look like a white noise with humps in amplitude.

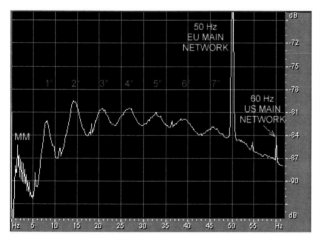

Spectrum analysis of the same six hour file. Here we can see the first seven Schumann resonances. Other signals apear in the spectrum: a strong 50Hz carrier from the European main network, a weak 60Hz tone probably from United States, and below 5Hz the microphonic effect caused by mechanical movement of the antenna in the wind.

The frequencies which are normally quoted for the first five resonances are of 7.8, 13.8, 19.7, 25.7, and 31.7Hz. As we can see there is not a perfect harmonic relationship between them (the second one is not exactly double the first one), but this is due to the fact that both the ionosphere and the earth's crust are penetrated to different extents at different frequencies. Also, they not well defined spectral lines, but they are frequency bands where the noise increases, like noise humps on the spectrum graph. The strength of these signal increments is related to the physical resonator quality, in this case the Earth-Ionosphere duct, and it is expressed in the same way as inductors in electronics, through a parameter, the quality factor "Q".

The value of the Q of the first resonance is 4, and those of the higher ones is greater, but their amplitude decreases as the frequency gets higher. This is due to the larger attenuation of higher frequencies during propagation. Therefore the first three resonances are easily identifiable, the fourth and the fifth less so and from the sixth they become lost in the background noise.

Due to solar radiation of the ionosphere and due to the gravitational effect of the Moon on the Earth, the resonant cavity dimensions are not constant. So we will have a small frequency shift of few tenth of hertz, and we will have a small variation in amplitude too. Schumann resonance parameters are constantly monitored by Berkeley University in California.

Schumann resonance intensity is around 1pT with variations at different times and places. That value would correspond to a 0.3mV/m electric field, but this equivalence is not always true because of the wavelength. As we will see later we are in the near field, that is the region quite close (relative to the wavelength) to the source generating the signal. In this condition the magnetic and electric component values do not follow the classic radio signal rules, valid for electromagnetic radiated signals.

Long distance spherics

As we saw in chapter three, much of the spherics' energy concentrates in the VLF band from 4 to 11kHz. Under 4kHz the spherics are increasingly attenuated, down to 2kHz, but with further decrease in the frequency, this phenomenon inverts and at few hundreds of hertz the spherics can travel long distances with very low attenuation.

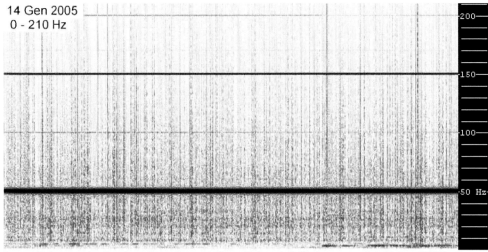

Long distance spherics, in a day where static activity at 4kHz is very quiet. Below 200Hz they appear strong and clear, and below 50Hz we can see Schumann resonances too.

Long distance spherics are sometimes associated with the higher frequency part of the spheric at 4kHz, and they sound like a whip-crack, very loud and close. At other times they are solitary and they sound like thunder in the storm or far off fireworks. While to a human ear they sound as confused as thunder, analyzing them with a spectrogram we can see aspects of amplitude and frequency we mentioned earlier. They are rather commonly received signals, mainly in summertime, when the electromagnetic activity is more intense due to the storms. They can also be very strong at more than 1000pT, that is 60dB beyond Schumann resonances, or a million times higher in power.

ELF Whistlers and Hiss

We mention them since many papers talk about this type of signal, even if we must admit they are very difficult to receive at medium latitudes. As for VLF, even this lower spectrum portion, has its whistlers, starting from 200Hz down to 20Hz, with maximum intensity between 80 and 90Hz. Unlike VLF whistlers the ELF variety are very slow, passing from 200 to 20Hz in as long a time as a minute. Their origin is connected to the solar wind action on the magnetosphere.

The situation is similar for hiss, which in this band has its maximum between 200 and 300Hz. It is sometimes difficult to distinguish because, graphically, it is very similar to Schumann resonances with increasing strength. The distinction is possible by observing the contrast in resonance spectrograms. When this decreases, in other words when resonances themselves are less pronounced, it is possible to identify a hiss.

Continuous magnetic pulsations

Here we mean terrestrial magnetic field variations, caused by phenomena occurring in the magnetosphere due to the effects of the solar wind. This hits the magnetosphere deforming it, causing magnetic field line relocation, perceivable at the ground as medium value variations. In the frequency band from 0.5 to 5Hz another phenomenon occurs, which is a kind of amplification of these signals up to 30dB due to the hydro-magnetic action (the gyro-ionic frequency but we will not cover that topic here). This effect makes it possible to receive 0.2 to 3Hz signals for periods often lasting some hours at a time.

A peculiar characteristic of these signals is that inside the magnetosphere, where they are generated, their propagation speed is 100 times slower than the speed of light. This is called Alfven speed (after its discover) and it has the weird characteristic of being a non-constant value. Let us return to the signal, and note that from the magnetosphere point where the signal is generated it proceeds in two opposite directions. By following the magnetic field line crossing that point, with the same transport mechanism as for hissing waves, it comes to the two geomagnetic conjugate points. At this moment if the signal can find a path through the ionosphere it is able to propagate to the ground. Then being trapped into the Earth-Ionosphere duct it is able to propagate for long distances away from the ionospheric entry point.

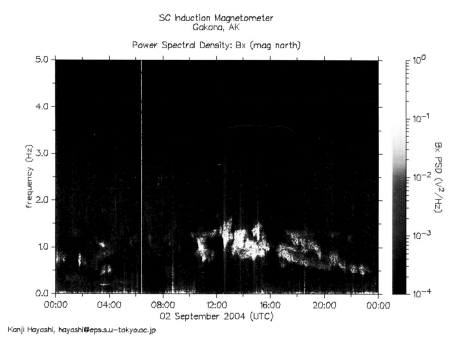

Kanji Hayashi, hayashi@eps.s.u-tokyo.ac.jp

A geomagnetic pulsation PC1. The emission, detected with a magnetometer by HAARP in Alaska. It is received at 0.5 to 2Hz. Source: www.haarp.alaska.edu.

The creation mechanism of these waves is due to the solar wind. which deforms the magnetosphere, and the non-constant speed during their birth can create hydro-magnetic signals which are very different from each other. These include whistlers (in this frequency range they are called pearl pulsations), choir, periodic and impulsive emissions, gurgles, sweepers (rising and falling tones) and other irregular or continuous emissions without any specific characteristic. They usually occur after a magnetic storm when the conditions return quiet, with a K index of 3 or less than 3.

13. Static fields and very slowly varying signals

Under 1Hz signals lose their oscillation aspect and become slow amplitude variations in time, lower still in frequency they are almost stationary.

Despite all this, even if under 1Hz, they are not commonly considered as signals. They are the radio expression of many physical phenomena, typical of these bands. In this case we lose the ability to have direct contact with the signal, losing the possibility of listening to what we have received. We can only represent them graphically as time or frequency functions. The receiver becomes a radio presenting the signal on a screen, the PC monitor.

At these low frequencies the choice of the electric or magnetic component makes a big difference to the kind of reception, mainly in the shape of the received signal as we will see below.

Stationary Electric fields

As we have already seen, the atmosphere has a 100V per meter electric field, which affects the ground, and it happens when the sky is blue. It is really because of this stationary field that a continuous current flows between the earth and the sky. The current flow is very small if we see it locally, but has very high levels if we calculate it over the whole planet. This electric field can be detected with a receiver, like an amplifier (for instance the ones for audio frequency signal direct reception), which are able to work down to zero frequency, that is continuous signal detecting.

The stationary electric field has some variations between day and night and it is influenced by temperature and air humidity, but above all it goes crazy when there are storm clouds. Clouds, even before they come over our heads, give notice of their stormy intentions. The electric field inverts its polarity going from +100V/m to –1000V/m.

Stationary electric field variations are strictly linked to what is above our heads. Its state can give valuable indications about how storms start and develop and also about how the ground morphology influences this charge. Its behaviour changes a lot when observed on the plain or on top of a mountain.

When we get ready to receive the electric potential in the air, we have also a second target, which is to know when certain limit values are exceeded, because this gives us advance information about when atmospheric conditions are suitable for creating cloud to ground lightning. Antennas and very sensitive receivers such as those for Radio Nature with PC audio cards connected to them, don't tolerate these kinds of events. So having a warning, which permits us to switch everything off, can make the difference between a working station and a storm burnt-out one.

When a station is left to operate unattended, acquiring data without the continuous presence of the operator, a static field receiver can be the solution for temporarily closing the station during the storm. The receiver will automatically return to work after the storm, once the good weather conditions return.

Terrestrial magnetic field variations

This subject is extremely extensive, and a whole book would be necessary to do justice to it. The basic mechanisms are complex and require a very deep knowledge of space physics. We will just describe the main signals and you will find references at the end of this book to enable you to dig deeper into the processes which form these signals.

While the electric field provides us with information mainly about local conditions, the terrestrial magnetic field contains messages arriving from very far away, mainly from the sun. The terrestrial magnetic field originates from core electric currents. The solar wind, which is also an electric current, creates a huge magnetic field, as large as a planet, with field lines extending into the surrounding space, and forming an area around the Earth called the Magnetosphere. The magnetic field intensity at medium latitudes is about 47000nT, which is almost 130dB stronger than the Schumann Resonance, which are five million times weaker. Its intensity varies and these variations can be very different from each other.

There are periodical variations, due to the day and night cycle and due to the passage of the moon. The variations due to the sun are called daytime solar regular variations and they last 24 hours at between 10 and 80nT intensity. The variations due to the moon are called daytime lunar regular variations, they last 24 hours and 50 minutes with an intensity of one tenth of the solar variations. Last but not least, a periodic variation is linked to the solar cycle, with an 11 year period and an intensity of 10nT.

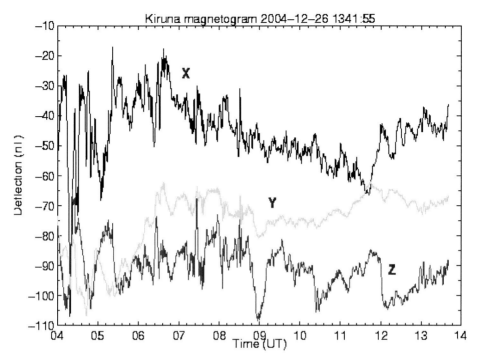

Ten hours of magnetic field variations, recorded by Kiruna observatory (North Europe). Top, middle and bottom lines represent the three axes reading: x, y and z.

On top of these are irregular variations which do not have a fixed period and which are connected to solar storms. This is the "wind" coming from the sun, and hitting the magnetosphere. These produce electric currents, which deform the terrestrial magnetic field and causes solar particles to precipitate. They are called "storm" or "bay" (these last ones for their peculiar form on the magnetogram) and they can have intensities varying from few dozens nT up to some five hundreds nT.

Magnetic pulsations

Another big group of magnetic signals are geomagnetic pulsations, which are field line oscillations produced by the solar wind energy. There are two principal types: irregular ones and continuous ones.

Irregular pulsations (in the books you'll find as Pi1 and Pi2) have a period varying from one second up to two and a half minutes, so the frequency range is from 1Hz to 7mHz (millihertz). The intensity is barely 0.1nT at equatorial latitudes but up to 100nT close to the poles. They are present during the night with a peak round midnight, and they are related to a magnetic storm presence.

The **regular pulsations** are maybe best known and they are called Continuous Pulsations. Their presence is typical during low solar activity periods. They originate in the part of the magnetosphere facing the sun and indicate a calm magnetosphere. They are divided into five frequency groups, with the following characteristics:

- <u>Type 1:</u> Continuous pulsations (PC1 we've talked about in the earlier section), have a period from 0.2 to 5 seconds and a frequency from 5 to 0.2Hz with a 0.05 to 0.1nT amplitude. They are receivable night and day on the whole Earth but mainly at high latitudes. Signals show as an oscillation train lasting from some minutes, up to a few hours and in geomagnetically conjugate points only.

- <u>Type 2:</u> Continuous pulsations (PC2) have a period going from 5 to 10 seconds, and a frequency from 200 up to 100mHz, with intensity between 0.1 and 2nT and they are receivable from local sunrise to midday.

- <u>Type 3:</u> Continuous pulsations (PC3) have a period from 10 to 45 seconds, and a frequency from 100 to 22mHz , with an intensity from 0.1 to 2nT. They are receivable in geomagnetic conjugate points between sunrise and midday.

- <u>Type 4:</u> Continuous pulsations (PC4) have a period from 45 to 150 seconds, with a frequency from 22 to 7mHz and they are more intense than those above, from 2 to 20nT.

- Finally <u>type 5:</u> Continuous pulsations (PC5) are also called giant pulsations; they have a period going from two and a half minutes to ten minutes, with a frequency from 6.7 to 1.7mHz and they can be rather intense from 5 to 500nT. They are a typical phenomenon of the very first hours of the daylight.

14. Man-made signals in the ELF and ULF bands

It would be natural for us to ask what artificial signals can achieve at such low frequencies, where transmission conditions are very difficult and equipment prohibitively expensive. We find some interesting answers.

Communications to submarines

This subject is very particular and we cannot avoid inserting it in this book. Firstly because it is a unique transmission system and secondly because signals arrive strongly and clearly over most parts of the planet. They end up captured in some spectrograms so it is important to know how to recognise them.

The necessity of sending messages to submarines without forcing them to come to the surface, a manoeuvre that would have been dangerous because they would be immediately detectable, gave the impulse to low frequency study and research. We can date the beginning of this need in 1960 when Polaris A1, the first atomic submarine with on board nuclear warheads, mounted on intercontinental ballistic missiles, sailed from the Florida coast towards oceanic depths.

The submarine communication problem is not easy to solve, because salt water absorbs radio frequency signals and completely destroys every conventional radio signal just one metre below the water surface. The only frequencies able to penetrate the superficial layer and reach the greater sea depths, are very low ones because of their long wavelengths. A 76Hz radio signal has 0.3dB/m attenuation in sea-water and so permits global coverage.

Transmission of this kind of signal is achieved by two worldwide coverage transmitter sites, one operating on 82Hz in frequency based on the Kola peninsula (Northern Europe) and even now used by Russia. The other one at 76Hz is installed in Northern America and is composed of a double installation with one in Wisconsin and the second in Michigan. These were used until 2004 by the United States. The wavelength of about 4000 kilometres and the limited attenuation, which is a characteristic of such low frequency emissions, permits these two stations to have worldwide coverage from only one transmission site.

The biggest problem the technicians of the two superpowers were called upon to solve was finding an adequate antenna to radiate such an unusual signal. Even very high pylons (several hundreds of metres), used by the army for RTTY transmissions on VLF frequencies, were useless if we consider a 4000km wavelength. The solution was to inject signals into the ground, like long dipole placed on the soil, with extremities connected to the ground.

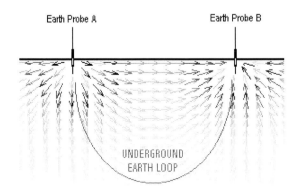

Electrical scheme of an ELF transmitting antenna, realised with two earth probes. A current flux flows between the probes in the underground layers of the soil.

To work as transmitting antenna the distance from A to B must be at least a few dozens of kilometres.

Some sites were located where the ground conductivity was low (for instance the Precambrian rock in Wisconsin) to distribute the currents along deep paths. The physical dimensions are impressive. The Russian antenna is formed from two 60 kilometers long arms with foundations dug for several kilometers. This way, the current goes deeply into the ground and the transmitter injects currents of between 200 and 300 amperes into the ground. A high conductivity in the deepest layers provides a long and deep path for the current, and thus a high antenna efficiency. Surface currents would decrease the system gain. We can consider this antenna as a buried loop, the deeper the currents can be made to flow the bigger the area, and the higher the efficiency, of the loop.

The American system, not modified after 1989, started with a capital investment of 500 million dollars, and it cost 15 million dollars per year to run. This system used two antennas operating at the same time. One was in Wisconsin composed of two lines, one of 22km and one of 44km in length. The Stanford Research Institute made a survey and according to them, the Russian system had a better efficiency of about 10dB compared to the American one.

Submarine on-board reception

Submarine on-board reception has some severe difficulties. The working area of a submarine is a screened metal tube. Basically there are three methods for receiving ELF signals in submerged submarines. The first one is with a 305 metre long cable, unrolled from the lower part of the submarine dragged like a tail by another 100 metre length cable. The longest one has conductive ends due to a metallic coil a few centimeters long at the cable extremity.

The dragged antenna can collect the voltage difference from the two points in the water 305 metres apart. The signal, is then fed into the second cable transporting it back into the submarine to the radio receiver systems, it is amplified by one or more amplifiers placed inside this cable. Everything has to be smooth and continuous to avoid a possible entanglement when it is towed, and externally it looks like just one 405 metre long single cable. This system has a very high sensitivity but a problem could occur if the submarine had to execute any sudden changes of direction.

The second method consists of a Hall sensor located in a kind of lance mounted at the submarine bow, and which is separated from the hull to avoid the noise pick-up from the submarine's machinery.

A worrying picture of the Hall sensor, placed on the bow of the USS Seawolf submarine, 1963.

Finally, a more recent method is using an on-hull loop which consists of a small coil wrapped on a mu-metal core and placed inside of a special resin tube to attenuate the mechanical vibrations transmitted from the hull. The tube is fixed inside a metallic U-shaped supporting the structure.

Conductive extremity of a submarine cable antenna. The rounded end avoids the snagging on the ocean floors

105

Transmissions on 76 and 82Hz are mono-directional, directed only towards submerged mobile units. The submarines are not able to transmit back and for full communication they must surface and use conventional frequencies.

The modulation used for these transmissions is a frequency shift type, where a single tone is transmitted whose frequency is moved in time, in a few tenths of Hz steps. Given that reception conditions are critical, the signal is received with very narrow filters to improve the signal/noise ratio. This technique improves the clarity, but at the same time it slows down the information speed of the system. A receiver with a 5mHz wide frequency filter, takes almost three and a half minutes to detect the presence of a signal. This is the reason why signals on these frequencies are transmitted very slowly and a message composed of 6 tones of ten minutes duration each will last an hour.

The attenuation suffered by the signal during propagation is known. This comes from mathematical calculations and is then verified in the field. It is weird to notice the propagation effect of a signal traveling between the ionosphere and the ground, where the intensity decreases as soon as you move away from the transmitter, but increases after we reach a distance of 14,000 kilometres due to the Earth lens effect. At the antipodes to the transmission point, the signal is concentrated again by addition of waves coming in from all directions.

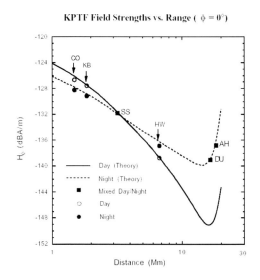

The graph shows how the signal at 82Hz and at 76Hz is attenuated according to the transmitter distance (expressed in thousands of kilometres).

The dotted line indicates the attenuation over a nocturnal path, while the continuous one shows a diurnal path.

From: *Reception of ELF Signals at Antipodal Distances*, by Antony C. Fraser-Smith, STAR Laboratory, Stanford University, and Peter R. Bannister, Nebraska Circle

In Europe, the Russian transmitter signals arrive clearly and with an intensity of 20dB greater than the background noise, using a 10mHz resolution (therefore technically it is available on every PC).

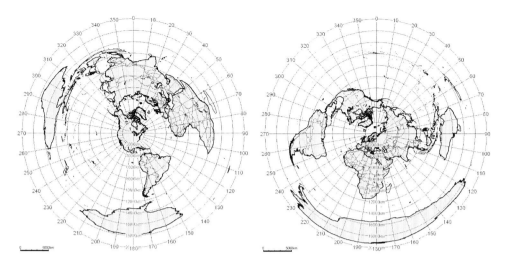

The World, shown as a Great Circle projection as it is seen by two ELF band transmitters: American (Wisconsin-Michigan) and Russian (Kola).

The American station is 7500 kilometers distant from European territory. Its signal, weaker at the beginning due to the less efficient transmission system, arrives with us in Europe with a 0.04pT intensity, in other words almost 70 times weaker than the Russian signal, and it is very difficult to distinguish from the hum noise.

It is very difficult to receive this signal in Europe. It only appeared on very high resolution spectrograms, as a hardly visible trace, appearing and disappearing and confused in the background noise. The American system was abandoned on 30 September 2004 and it was replaced both by VLF and higher frequency band transmissions, and by HAARP type station transmissions. We also have to add to this list laser satellite communications. Probably no longer used strategically with the end of the cold war.

Railroad signals, American mains network and computers

The Norwegian rail system supplies its engines with a 16kV alternating current at 16.66 Hz. The signal from these supplies reaches all over Europe, but mainly at night-time. A weak tone appears right above the second Schumann Resonance, with a slowly varying signal. The signal can be received for hours or can disappear after half an hour. Notice that the frequency of 16.66Hz is exactly one third of the European power supply frequency of 50 Hz.

This is not the only signal coming from railroads. Many track-signaling commands use very low frequencies and propagate using the rails, and the aerial electric lines. If we have a listening session close to a railway (a few dozen kilometres from the rail track) it is possible to receive these tones at 1.8Hz, 3.5Hz, and 5.3Hz.

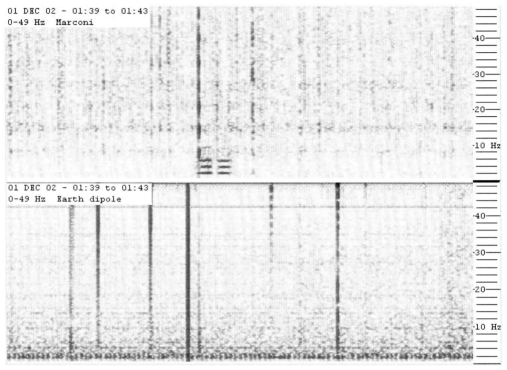

The upper part of this image shows wire antenna reception of three railway tones under the first Schumann Resonance. The lower part shows the same reception made with an earth dipole where the signals are not present.

In the picture we can also compare the reception with a Marconi antenna where we can see both the Schumann Resonance and the railway tones (a dozen dB above the hum noise), and with a 30 metre earth dipole where the noise prevails.

Another signal we can find in Europe at night-time and in the early hours of the morning is the 60Hz tone coming from the American continent, radiated by the power supply network. It is possible perhaps that Americans can receive European network signals. The signal has better propagation conditions at night time and this is the reason why the intensity is higher in the middle of the night.

Similar to the signals mentioned above, but sometimes of higher intensity, are the tones radiated by the tube of a PC video-monitor at the "refresh" frequency, where 60, 70, 72, 75, 85 and 100Hz are the most common signals. A 17 inch video-monitor CRT signal can propagate for hundreds of metres when the monitor is working.

A last signaling concerns typical sequences tones (25 Hz in Italy, 20 Hz in USA, 16.67 in UK…), regularly spaced and lasting few seconds, which are radiated by phone lines and they are used to effect ringing.

Mains network mirrors

The study of frequencies under 100/120Hz can be misleading, because even best researchers can make a mistake. It is very common to find under 50Hz the presence of tones that are clearly artificial, of very stable frequency, with a strong signal and with regular beat, such as an 18Hz tone which repeats every 30 seconds (on–off) for ten seconds and then disappears for the whole day. If the reception system is recording data with a spectrogram up to 40Hz, we can clearly see that the tone is spectrally pure, and there are no 36Hz harmonics. There are no other close by emissions and by disconnecting the antenna the signal disappears (so is really being captured by the antenna). Signals such as the one described have surprised more than one researcher, thinking they have, for the first time, discovered some weird system perhaps of military origin.

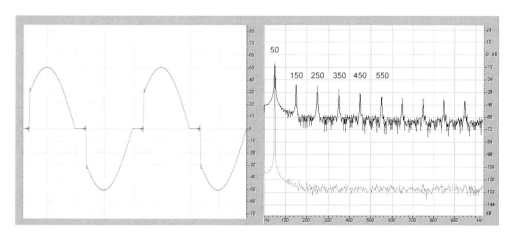

On the left is an oscillogram of a sine wave regulated by lamp-dimmer at 50Hz. On the right is a pure sine spectrum (on the bottom) and the spectrum in frequency after a power regulation (on the top): the hum noise has increased and we have many more strong odd harmonics at 150, 250, 350Hz.

The explanation, in 98% of the cases were less fascinating. Different pumping systems, gasworks and waterworks, or simply big industry machinery systems working with electric motors, always need a power regulator to control the power of the motors. Let us consider, for instance, a pumping system where the pressure must be kept constant despite the continuous variation in load presented by the pump. The motor must stop pressure decreasing due to the loading and so it needs a continuous alternating current regulator.

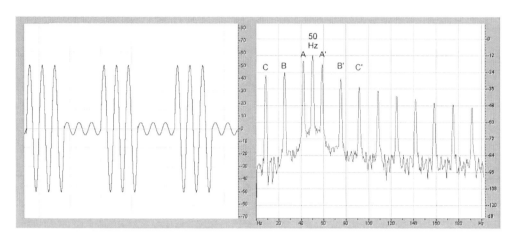

Whole-cycle burst power regulation effect: we can notice many mirrored at 50 Hz.

The most common systems for regulating a motor's power, is whole-cycle burst regulation. A control circuit selects the number of cycles of sine wave allowed to pass, according to the required power. For instance three cycles pass and three of them are stopped, supplying the motor with 50% of the available power.

In practice, it is as though the regulator "presses the on and off button" many times a second, making the final average current less than 100% and making the interruptions always fall when the instantaneous voltage is zero. In industrial motors a similar system can control powers of up to 20 megawatts for each motor.

This kind of regulation introduces into the electrical power mains supply a large quantity of high level harmonics. For example together with 50Hz mains frequency are intermediate frequencies between 0 and 50Hz and between 50 and 100Hz, which are generated depending on the rate of switching of the regulator. The regulator produces a kind of amplitude modulation of the mains power signal and the resulting noise is very similar to AM modulation. It appears as two sidebands around the carrier frequency (50Hz), which is the network frequency.

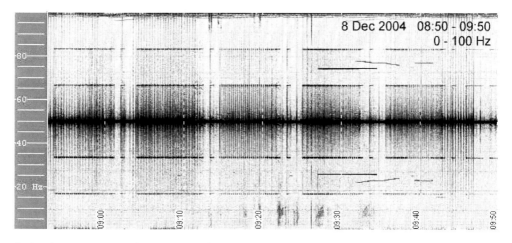

A signal spectrogram using an earth dipole in the 0-100Hz range: mirrored signals are clearly seen around the central 50Hz frequency. Received in Cumiana (Turin- Italy).

Signals generated this way are always "mirrored" to the electrical mains power frequency. If we find a 20Hz tone, we will find another corresponding one at 80Hz, and if the tone is at 41Hz, it is mirrored at 59Hz and so on. This is the reason why is not convenient to do narrow band monitoring if we are to correctly interpret the source to these signals. It is also important to consider the portion up to 100 or 120Hz. If the band is very narrow, as for instance in between 5 and 10 Hz, it is better to open a second window with a second spectrogram displaying the mirrored band from 90 to 95Hz.

This way we can exclude 98% of the signals that we would have catalogued as "mysterious". Anyone can be deceived, but at least we are sure not to misinterpret a lathe as a submarine, or a purifier pump as a seismic precursor. Since this kind of signal travels through the electricity mains power distribution network, it is very insidious if we use magnetic field antennas for reception, such as loop or earth dipoles. Electric field reception systems are much safer, using a whip or wire antennas.

A last trap comes from devices used in the metal industry to melt steel. The melting of the metal is effected by the inserting the object to be melted into a very strong magnetic field, generated by high power coils fed with current pulsed at a few hertz in a square wave. These are often referred to as induction furnaces. The spectrum produced by a hundred kilowatt load (pulsed at few hertz) is enormous and, despite the filters, these crucibles have extremely strong spurious components.

The power regulation produces sub-harmonics and a huge hum noise. This explains the limitations of several filters in cleaning reception corrupted by mains power signals. It is very often not enough to eliminate carrier frequencies superimposed in spectrogram on the hum noise, but it is more important to move

111

away from electrical lines to reduce the general noise effect. This is not always a simple thing to do, if you live in densely population zone.

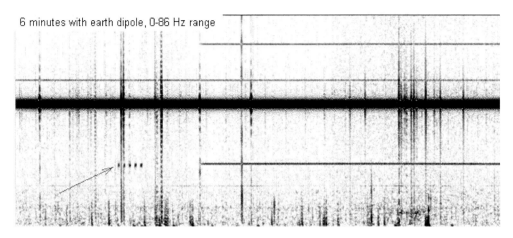

In an earth dipole acquired spectrogram in the 0 to 86 Hz range there appears a weird five tones sequence at 25Hz, caused by a call (ring-tone) on phone line.

The HAARP research activity

If you have studied VLF, you must have heard about HAARP (High Frequency Active Auroral Research Program), though not always with reliable information, because of the military secrecy imposed on some of this research. In the past there was also the rumour of some modifications of the earth magnetic field being due to this station. Thankfully none of these things have ever happened.

HAARP is a scientific research station working since the early 1990s, sited in Alaska, and it works to receive many parameters such as static fields up to VLF, by using electric component receivers, magnetometers, riometers, radars, ionoprobes and several meteorological devices. A visit to the web-site (http://www.haarp.alaska.edu/) gives a good idea of the daily data collected by this centre.

What has been of great interest, and still is (talking as an environmentalist), are the transmission activities of this center. The station has a transmitter capable of 3.6 million watts power in the HF range (starting from 2.8 up to 10MHz) and a very impressive antenna system. This highly efficient antenna system (so efficient it can radiate the ionosphere with only a 5° beam width and with a 30dB gain) at HAARP is able to radiate towards the sky something like three and a half billion watts. Yes, toward the sky, because the objective of this center is the excitation of a limited area of the ionosphere and the study of the physical processes occurring there.

The Haarp wood antenna: it is impressive, but it allows a huge saving compared to the length of a transmitting dipole for submarine signals.
Picture from: *http://www.haarp.alaska.edu/haarp/images*

It could seem a complicated process, but, if we consider that the HF radiation effects in the sky are to produce an ELF signal (the one used for the submarines), the true purpose of this scientific research becomes clearer. It is the production of a very low frequency signal, able to reach submerged submarines over the whole of the globe, without the need for the huge antennas that we described in the preceding chapters. The technique consists of irradiating the E layer of the ionosphere, between 80 and 100 kilometers in altitude, with a strong radio frequency signal. Normally in this region, millions amperes of currents flow, originated from the magnetosphere.

The HAARP radio wave flux tends to decrease the capacity of this region of the ionosphere to conduct this current flux, so it is diverted on an alternative path for the period that external signal is present. When the signal is switched off the currents quickly resume their natural paths.

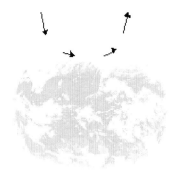

The on-off rhythm of the HAARP signals induces the emission of a corresponding ELF/ULF frequency. If the beam at 3.2MHz is turned on and off with a 12.5Hz rhythm, a 12.5Hz ULF signal is produced, made by continuous modulation of the natural auroral current. This way has been possible to indirectly radiate signals up to 30kHz in frequency. The transmission efficiency is very low.

If we excite the atmosphere with a 1 million watt HF signal, we will have a 10mW ELF/ULF signal emission (we lose about 80dB). HAARP emissions in ELF/ULF are very weak with signals at ground level of 1 to 3 pico-Tesla, which is very close to background noises and the Schumann Resonances.

The Alaskan installation, although the best known, is not the only one for these kinds of experiments. There has also been one at Platteville since 1970, also Arecibo, Sura, Tromsoe and Hipas with powers ranging from 750kW to 1.6MW at 25MHz and with antenna gains of up to 28dB. The planned installation of Hiscat, Sweden, should reach 35dB gain with 10MW transmitters and an effective radiated signal power close to 30GW (30 billion Watt). It is truly difficult to comprehend the costs and dimensions of these installation, if it were not for military investments.

114

15. Seismic precursors

Sometimes a seismic event uses all its strength to destroy all our activities, and in these cases we must ask the question, why is it possible that despite all our technology, we still are not able to forecast an earthquake?

We will not discuss water diviners or magicians, but there are three main scientific lines of thought. First the study of the phenomenon seen from its mathematical and statistical side, then the study of weak seismic shakes and of seismic phenomena preceding the earthquake, and the third is the monitoring of radio emissions at VLF occurring just before the earthquake.

How radio precursors are generated

The physics of materials and a knowledge of the structure of the Earth's surface can give us some explanation of how a future earthquake might emit radio signals or affect existing emissions such as the radio broadcast transmissions.

A very first hypothesis concerns the piezo-electric effect in some rocks. This is used in piezoelectric lighters, where the electricity producing the spark for ignition is generated by the compression of a crystal. Similarly rocks under pressure would generate high voltages and sparks, which could radiate as radio signals, and electron emissions. Those radio signals would be directly receivable, whilst the electron emission should affect the propagation of existing signals. In practice this theory is not applicable everywhere because not all rocks are piezoelectric and so this system would only be useful in some places.

A second hypothesis, which may be more applicable, finds some precursor signals in micro fractures produced in rocks under pressure. The fracture of the chemical bonds could provoke the creation of strong electric field. The fractal nature of these fractures would also allow a large radiating efficiency by generating signals receivable both from subsoil and from the air. This hypothesis would also explain why usually precursors disappear just before the earthquake. The micro-fractures would fill with water, which would prevent radiation just before the final rupture. The currents circulating in the ground near the surface could be influenced.

A variant to this second hypothesis links the radio impulse production to mechanical vibrations preceding the rupture of the rock under pressure. This phenomenon is called "rock crying".

Some other theories suppose a possible effect on the ionosphere caused by the slow moving of wide areas of earth. The perturbation would happen at an altitude between 70 and 90km, with the consequent intensity variation of the signals propagating between earth and ionosphere.

An other hypothesis suggests that rock energy and surface layer movements would induce variations in the terrestrial magnetic field, detectable directly by magnetometer, or through their effect on radio signal propagation. Those are just hypothesis of physicists and geologists, but in reality what does happen?

Laboratory tests

The most revealing test to make consists of taking a rock, crushing and shattering it to check if it emits a "radio crying". This experiment is easy to imagine but not easy to do. The tests done in Italy, for instance, are well documented and have produced the following results.

At the Pavia University (Italy), under the direction of Prof. E Mognaschi, a rock cube is submitted of single axes pressure by a press up to its breaking point. A simple ferrite antenna was used and emissions starting from 200kHz and to over 2.5MHz are received for over half of the process which brought the rock to shattering point.

This same experience has been repeated in the Italian State Railroad experimental laboratory and it was obtained the same results even though it used different types of rock, that were not all piezoelectric. The maximum levels of the signals in this case were received in the VHF band at 230MHz and less evident on lower frequencies at 3.9MHz and in the UHF range at 460MHz. Signals were made up of single impulses or short bursts, starting at around 50% of the breaking load, then becoming more and more intense, ending up with the rock shattering under the pressure.

Similar results have been documented by Doc. A. Nardi, who has shattered different kinds of rock cubes revealing their radio emissions. He also verified the presence of wide-band VLF signals during mine explosions, used in a cave to extract limestone. Starting from 100Hz the intensity was strong at low frequencies, but it decreased as soon as the frequency increased.

We can affirm that there is physical evidence for the validity of these models, but when we are in a practical field, there is some confusion because of the huge quantity of documented evidence often with very contradictory results. There does seem little doubt that rock crushing produces radio waves and we know from early radio experiments that sparks will generate radiation up to microwave frequencies.

It is in many ways not surprising that different rocks cut in different ways and crushed in different equipments, probably at different rates, yield different results.

Experiences in the field

a) Geo electrical voltage potentials

This concerns the study of geo-electric potentials and terrestrial magnetic field variations in risk zones. A southern French survey network, several Chinese monitoring stations and Greek researchers, using earth probes for an antenna with variable spacing distances (from 20 to 100 meters) document variations of the voltage measured due to seismic events of magnitude greater than five (Richter scale). The geo-electric potential, with its surface current variations running in the ground, would be able to give indications of where the seismic stresses are building up within an approximate radius of 50km, and also on when the event would be likely to occur within a time range of 7 to 115 hours. The received signal band in this case goes from the DC to few dozens of hertz.

A worldwide organization working in this direction, called ELFRAD is constituted of amateur operators. The group has defined a standard data collecting system with an acquisition card (ADC) to connect to the PC and used it to read the voltage between two earth stakes, a hundred meters apart and oriented North-South.

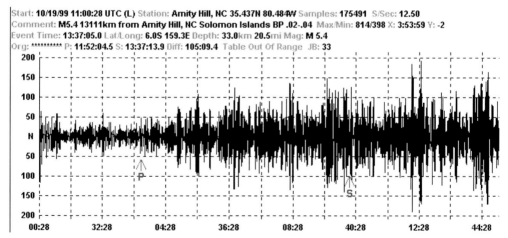

An example of an automatic acquisition of signal with time between two earth stakes. From the ELFRAD website: www.elfrad.com

This organization claims to regularly receive radio seismic precursors over the whole globe. The occasional presence on their site of some articles near to the mystic (such as aliens or thought transmission from continent to continent) suggests that their conclusions should be taken with some caution. The system is, however, technically interesting and it will be discussed more deeply later on in the section on SLF band static field receivers.

According to many American Institutes, and in agreement with data collected by Illinois and California, the geo-electric current variations would also provoke oscillations of the terrestrial magnetic field's vertical component, with oscillations at about 1Hz detectable even thousands of kilometres away from the propagating seismic point.

b) Radio signal emissions

Californian universities such as Stanford, which study this phenomenon, report the presence of electromagnetic noise at low frequencies from 0.01 to 10Hz before an earthquake. The signal intensity would decrease when the frequency increases from 10Hz to 32kHz and it would only be occasionally detectable at these higher frequencies.

In Italy a group of radio amateurs in Lunigiana (Italy), report the presence of impulsive audio noise in the range between 20Hz and 50kHz, receiving it with a large vertical loop. The impulsive signal, which starts a few hours before the seismic event, ends just before the event. The same would be detectable with an electric antenna, such a wire antenna, recording the noise around 20Hz. Synchronized recordings of the same event, done with a vertical electric antenna, at the Pavia University would measure about the same plot of the noise from under 5Hz down to 0.01Hz (continuous current).

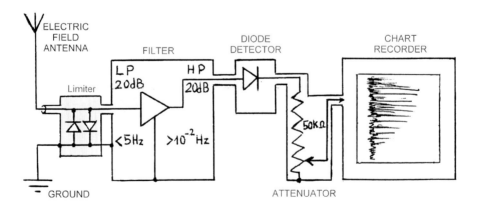

A block schematic of the system for seismic precursor monitoring, from the Pavia University (E: Mognaschi). The system records on paper the electric field noise from 10mHz to 5Hz.

Again in Greece some systematic observations have been reported, obtained with coils as antennas for magnetic signals under 20Hz. In this case the signal appear on the spectrogram, not as an impulsive noise, but as a horizontal parallel series of weak traces, like the imprint left by a cat's claws.

Strong signals are also observed in Italy (M. Eleuteri), very similar to a crackling rustle. These precursors have started two days before an event fifty kilometers away and they grew in intensity and frequency (repetition rate). The signals were received at up to 150MHz with 0.4mV intensity in the 24 hours before the event actually occurred.

One of the very first observations done of this type is dated 1960 when five American radio telescopes, very far from each other and tuned on 18MHz (for the cosmic noise study) simultaneously received the same signal. It was discovered later that the signal came from Chile where shortly afterwards a big earthquake occurred.

Looking at more recent data, Intercosmos Russian satellites would receive electromagnetic emissions in the upper atmosphere, similar to noise in the frequency range from 100Hz to 20kHz, right above the seismic epicenter, starting a few hours before the event. These emissions, we may suppose, could be created by a high energy electron flux (also observed), coming from rocks in the pre-rupture phase.

c) Propagation effects

Many studies also talk about this effect, which suggests mechanisms occurring in run-up to an earthquake, in the surface layers would perturb the ionosphere with a direct effect on some signal propagation.

Hiroshima University reports for example of FM broadcast signal variations when the signal path crosses an area where the earthquake is developing. The received signal starts to oscillate by some decibels the day before the event, and it increases to a dozen decibels and then decreases once the earthquake has ended. To discriminate between precursors and other causes, we must check three frequencies, two with signals coming from very distant stations and one clear of any signals. The system would be effective up to 45km from the epicenter when the earthquake is of magnitude 6 or more.

Once more in Japan, at the Tokyo Space Agency, variations are reported in signals of a few kHz, when these signals cross a zone where an earthquake is developing. The suggested cause would be the release of radon gas. This process would only be valid for seismic events close to the surface, occurring only in the first 30km ground depth. The calculation method is very complex. VLF signals naturally oscillate in intensity, particularly on long journeys, with oscillations periods from 2 to 28 days called planetary atmospheric waves, or M.J.O. (Madden

Julian Oscillation). When a seismic event is imminent the amplitude of the oscillations increases, and this would indicate that a pre-seismic anomaly is in progress.

Observations have also been carried out in Italy with positive results in 1997/8 (by Bari Roma and Sheffield Universities) during seismic events in Umbria and Marche regions. Tests were done by monitoring long wave signals at 189kHz, 246kHz and 270kHz respectively coming from Catanissetta (RadioDue), MonteCarlo and Chech Republic. Again in this case, a few days before the event some strong variations in intensity were observed, so we can suppose they were a consequence of the anomalies induced by the developing earthquake on the ionosphere. Unlike the preceding observations, for the very first time, the effect was reported on an earthquake occurring widely over a 50km radius.

Why does no reliable prediction method exist yet?

Despite the observations described above, it is clear that the seismic precursor mechanisms induce barely detectable effects. The small increase in signal strength of a distant radio station, could be caused by a pre-seismic event, but it could also be the result of a transmitter defect, or it could be due to the humidity on the antenna or to a van parked below the transmitter antenna mast, or to the presence of fog or very heavy rain on the signal path.

It is very difficult to directly relate a weak indicator to an earthquake, without the certain ability to discriminate between a genuine precursor and all these other environmental or human factors which could produce a similar effect. It is probable that the observations made by the different university institutes (cited above) are all correct. There is however a great difficulty in understanding how those research results can become a reliable forecasting method. It is as though we would receive a couple letters per week by mail indicating the date, place and time of an earthquake. In any year we would receive some hundred letters, but only two of them would tell the truth. How could we use this information? Most likely there would be no way to use them alone.

We have a similar situation with the hum noise monitoring in ULF, ELF and VLF bands and with seismic current study. This was once thought to be a hypothetical precursor, but how can we distinguish it from all these natural phenomena generating radio waves of a similar kind?

If, for instance, we observe a sudden variation in ground currents, that is in the voltage read between two earth probes a hundred metres apart. We need to be sure that it is not caused by the vertical electric field (possibly a charge cloud passing over our heads), or caused by a terrestrial magnetic field variation due to high solar activity, or by an electro-chemical effect in the ground (maybe it has rained few kilometers away), or by a temperature variation in the receiving station area.

We need therefore to observe a large number of events, so large that it will allow us the certainty of recognizing a real precursor and of distinguish it from a false signal. What a hard task! If we wish to radio-phonically forecast only the occurrence of strong and intense earthquakes, and thankfully they are very rare, we would require much time and expense. We could forecast this kind of event if we install a PC (working in unattended operation) for this activity only, running twenty four hours a day… for several years.

Monitoring at home

The mission is very compelling but with no certain final results. We can though, do something and we do not need to be a University or a Research Institute for this. If we have an old, slow, unused PC after calculating the cost of its permanent use, we can equip a monitoring station in a quick and simple way.

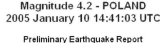

Magnitude 4.2 - POLAND
2005 January 10 14:41:03 UTC

Preliminary Earthquake Report
U.S. Geological Survey, National Earthquake Information Center
World Data Center for Seismology, Denver

A light earthquake occurred at 14:41:03 (UTC) on Monday, January 10, 2005. The magnitude 4.2 event has been located in POLAND. (This event has been reviewed by a seismologist.)

Magnitude	4.2
Date-Time	Monday, January 10, 2005 at 14:41:03 (UTC) = Coordinated Universal Time Monday, January 10, 2005 at 3:41:03 PM = local time at epicenter Time of Earthquake in other Time Zones
Location	51.525°N, 16.086°E
Depth	5 km (3.1 miles) set by location program
Region	POLAND
Distances	80 km (50 miles) NW of Wroclaw, Poland 115 km (70 miles) SSW of Poznan, Poland 120 km (75 miles) E of Cottbus, Germany 350 km (215 miles) WSW of WARSAW, Poland
Location Uncertainty	horizontal +/- 4.3 km (2.7 miles); depth fixed by location program
Parameters	Nst= 44, Nph= 44, Dmin=77.8 km, Rmss=0.85 sec, Gp= 43°, M-type=body magnitude (Mb), Version=Q
Source	USGS NEIC (WDCS-D)
Event ID	ustccq

Documents about a seismic activity posted on the web page of USGS, the US geological warning service. Monitoring is worldwide and covers the entire planet. Source: http://www.usgs.gov

The presence of numerous seismic networks sharing their data on the net, allows everyone access to the detailed list of all earthquakes originating on our planet, and so we can compare our VLF data to single events. In a following chapter, discussing the network observatory, we will give some site addresses with information about the Italian and southern Europe seismic activity as an example.

First of all we have to think about the receiver, because we do not exactly know what data to look for. Seismic precursors are observed in the audio band with both electric and magnetic (loop) antennas. The monitoring can be very elementary, made for instance by an automatic spectrogram saved at programmed times.

Once an earthquake has occurred we have to see whether the graphics correspond to the time of the event and then the ones from earlier hours or days, looking at the images for traces of possible anomalous signals to correlate to the earthquake. This must be repeated for each earthquake and so, after some experience, we can store the records a number of events as reference.

A more complex analysis method, without requiring anything additional for reception, can be applied to the signal plotting. We can generate elaborate spectrograms automatically, and we can also generate detailed graphics showing the variation of some values in time. In this case what appears in the screen is the electronic equivalent of the old paper-chart data plotter.

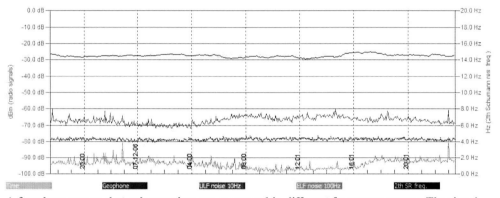

A four hour screen shot, where noises are compared in different frequency ranges. The signal was acquired with a Marconi vertical antenna and has been processed with SpectrumLab software.

In this case also, the choice can be vast, given that a single PC with an audio card permits the simultaneous monitoring of 20 different frequency ranges. If, for instance, we use a simple electric field receiver with a one metre whip (able to receive frequencies from 20Hz to 20kHz), we can monitor signal levels emitted by RTTY military sources, such as BGR, JXN, SQA, RDL, VTX3, and others. We can also simultaneously record medium noise levels for different frequency portions, for example from 20Hz to 2kHz, from 2 to 4kHz or else the signal maximum picked at a given interval, or fix a threshold level after which the PC generates an alarm. The possibilities are endless.

122

We reiterate the statements made earlier about environmental noises. The antenna must be placed very far away from electric lines, computers and cathode ray tubes. It is truly very hard to consider an effective monitoring station set up in these polluted conditions.

Some examples of the software it is necessary to use, will be discussed in a following chapter, when we will discuss unattended operation and SpectrumLab, which is freely downloadable software. The potential of this program allows for automatic data collection at a professional level. Fifteen years ago, a similar system with traditional instrumentation would have required a huge economic investment, impossible for a non professional researcher.

16. Receivers and antennas for the ELF and ULF bands

The reception system for frequencies between 1 and 100/120Hz is not very different from that used for receiving VLF. In this band, antennas and receivers start to perform less well because they are less sensitive. Signals at 82Hz for submerged submarines and Schumann Resonances are quite strong, but to receive them, the system must be made more sensitive than the one used so far for Radio Nature.

The electric field antenna

The combination of a 1 meter whip antenna and a simple electric field receiver is particularly successful, working without any problems from some hundreds of hertz up to the highest audio frequencies with good sensitivity, as we described in chapter three. This pairing of "short antenna/simple receiver" works perfectly if the antenna impedance (capacitive reactance) is comparable to the receiver input impedance. In electrical terms it is successful if the antenna is not influenced by the receiver connection which, given its high impedance, practically takes no power, that is the case down to some hundreds of hertz.

At frequencies less than 100Hz, the impedance of an electric field antenna is very high and it becomes much higher as the antenna becomes shorter compared with the wavelength. If we continue to use this same receiver, we will find that the signal from the antenna is reduced, because of the potential divider consisting of the antenna impedance and receiver input impedance. Therefore as soon as we get to low frequencies, the system becomes less sensitive.

An advertising slogan from the 1970s said that for painting a big wall a big brush is needed, and here we have just about the same thing. To get a big low frequency signal, we need a big antenna. In other words, if we use a bigger antenna, we can extend our range down to few hertz.

To work properly the antenna must form a large capacitance with the ground, which works as a reference. This way instead of the 8pF of the 1 meter whip, we can have the 65pF of an 8 metre vertical, and the result will be a 10 times lower frequency limit. If the 1m whip works down to 200Hz, then the 8 metre vertical will give the same sensitivity down to 20Hz.

It is not that easy to think of a very tall structure without considering the construction problems it gives us. It is one thing to install a couple of metres of vertical, but another thing entirely to install a 10 metre structure! We have two possible solutions, the first of which consists of using a fishing cane, which can be used to support a copper wire, the real antenna. Fishing canes without mountings, and very long, are available cheaply in big supermarkets. The cane can be fixed in a simple way to a two-metre stake, insulated at its base. In this simple and safe way we can construct a 10 metre vertical.

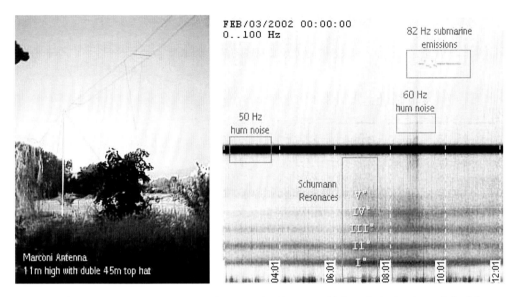

A Marconi T shaped antenna. The vertical part is 11 metres high and the horizontal double-wire hat 45 metres long. In the left part, the received signals: Schumann Resonance, 50Hz European mains, 60Hz of American mains and an 82Hz transmissions for submarines.

Another solution, which requires more effort, but gives better results comes from long wave radio amateur's antennas. They often use a "T" wire antenna structure called a Marconi. In this case we need two supports to support the antenna, which is made of wire only and so it is very light-weight. The vertical section is the active element of the whole system, able to receive or transmit according to the user's requirements, while the horizontal part, called a "capacity hat" hugely increases the system's capacitance to ground. A Marconi antenna 11 meter high with a 45 meter hat has a capacity to ground of about 400pF while the vertical has 40pF only.

Mathematically, by using a simple formula, we can calculate the lowest frequency limit the antenna/receiver system can reach, if we know the input impedance. This is possible because we have a resonant system. The elevated antenna works as electric field probe and so is electrically comparable to a simple RC network.

Flow = 1 / (2π * Rinput * Cantenna)

A practical example with a 1Mohm input resistance receiver and 1 meter whip, then with 8pF we obtain:

Flow = 1 / (6.28 * 10'000'000 * 8 * 10^{-12}) = 1990Hz

This is the lowest frequency that the system will reproduce with a flat frequency response, and below this frequency the performance decreases steadily. Suppose we can use the receiver down to 1000Hz with good performance. Then using the same formula we find out that with a 9 metre vertical we can go down to 100Hz and with a Marconi down to 15Hz. This frequency represents the limit of the system performance where the frequency response is flat. It can easily be used at even lower frequencies, but we know that display will show the signals as weaker and weaker, once we go beyond the calculated lower-limit frequency.

The electric field receiver

We must now re-design the receiver, because if we had connected a wire antenna to a BBB-4 receiver, we would have very easily saturated the input stage. So we would be listening both to Radio Nature signals, and to RTTY tones with long-wave music created by inter-modulation in the input stage. Receivers such as BBB-4 are not able to operate at such low frequencies. Their design decreases the sensitivity of the system for frequencies below 200Hz in order to filter out the hum noise caused by mains power distribution.

These receivers have also been conceived for use with portable recorders to listen to whistlers, chorus and tweaks, all of them in the audio band. All beyond this is regarded as "noise". Practical experience teaches us, that with portable recorders everything that is not a desired signal must be kept out. The less we have in the audio frequencies, the better the system works.

In the ELF region, the recorder is no longer usable, because at less than 100Hz the magnetic tape does not perform well and so we must use the PC audio card, which works in very linear way down to few hertz. This is convenient because we will need the PC to process the signal to display a useful representation.

The ELF frequencies are so low that they are no longer detectable by the human ear, but this has the useful consequence that we no longer need a big filtering system to remove undesirable signals. We record everything that enters the receiver, paying attention not to saturate it with very strong signals, and in the analysis phase we eliminate those signals that do not interest us.

Here you can see the circuit of a project for an electric field receiver able to go down to static field reception, able to tolerate very long wire antennas and yet be immune to inter-modulation phenomena.

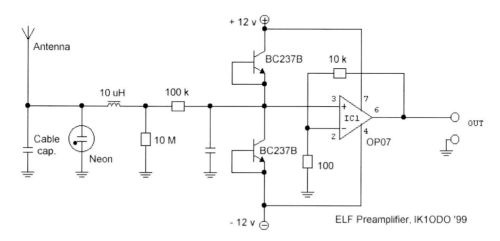

This circuit of a simple ELF receiver is able to accept the signal from a small whip, but also able to tolerate very long wire antennas without distortion (Marco Bruno's project, IK1ODO).

The antenna input capacitance represents the connection of the wire antenna, not a very short whip. It allows some dozens of metres of wire to be connected to the receiver. The small input neon bulb is the first protection for the integrated circuit, to a high and fast voltage transients (surges), such as lightning. A surge ionises the neon gas, which conducts the surge to ground to avoid burning-up the operational amplifier.

The 10μH inductance forms a block to higher frequency signals, to avoid them saturating the amplifier input, and provoking inter-modulation. We also have another low pass filter made of 100 kilohm resistor and 470pF capacitor performing the same function. The 10 Mohm resistance is in effect the load seen by the antenna and its value must therefore be as high as possible. The voltage on this resistance will drive the operational amplifier between pin three and ground, allowing also for a small bias current that is necessary for the operational amplifier to work.

The pair of BC237B transistors provides some further protection for the operational amplifier by working as a clipper for all those signals higher than 15V.

127

The system gain is established by the 10 kilohm and 100 ohm resistance ratio. Usually a gain of between 10 and 100 represents the right solution for most common types of audio card, when using the LINE input.

The OP07 precision operational amplifier works with very low bias current, so a large value resistance input can be used and also a high value of gain. The circuit will also work with the more common TL081 operational amplifier, by accepting a small increase in offset even though the noise figure is better.

If the antenna is big enough, the receiver becomes able to observe even the electric static field we mentioned in Chapter 1 where we talked about the terrestrial electrical field. If we connect a simple analogue meter to the receiver output, we can observe the presence of a voltage and also of strong variations in its value when storm clouds approach. We will cover this matter in more detail in the following chapter about static fields.

Even though this reception system goes down low in frequency, it retains a good sensitivity at high frequencies as well. So it is also appropriate for Radio Nature signal listening and for RTTY reception up to the highest frequency limit of the audio card.

There is, however, a different approach to building a bigger receiving antenna, a solution that is not always that easy to adopt. This consists of raising the input resistance of the receiver we wish to use. To do this we cannot use a common standard resistance at the input, such as the ones we can buy it in an electronics shop, since values usually available are not higher than 10 Mohm (millions of ohms). We have to employ a trick, which allows us to make a synthetic resistance of 50 Gigohm (billions ohm) with a transistor.

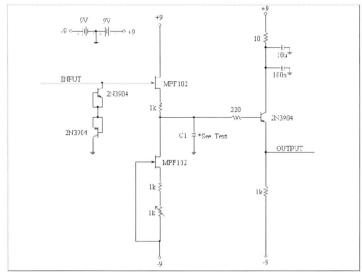

Scott Fusare's receiver with a very high input impedance. The input resistance, which in the previous circuit was 10 Mohm is replaced here by the two inverse junction transistors.

In the picture the 10 Mohm resistance of the previous circuit has been replaced by two 2N3904 transistors, which, connected this way, make a synthetic resistor of several hundreds Gigohm (billion ohm). An FET and a transistor do the amplification instead of the operational amplifier. We are able to receive signals with this circuit down to 1Hz in frequency, using only a 2 metre whip.

We must be very careful though, because the use of so high an impedance can generate other problems. We can no longer use antenna connectors with plastic insulation or even Teflon between the center pin and ground, given that even the high resistance of Teflon would be enough to short-circuit the signal. For the same reason, all the circuit around the antenna cannot make contact with a printed circuit board, but it must be suspended in the air.

Then the antenna must be soldered directly to the gate of the first FET, to reduce the unavoidable leakage current towards ground. It is also clear that even a little humidity is enough to "confuse" the receiver, mainly at the lower frequencies. It is the small antenna dimensions that force us to deal with these more critical parameters

Although this receiver was designed for very low frequencies, like the previous one it works very well over the whole VLF spectrum, right up to the top limit of the 22kHz audio card.

Big loops

Because electric-field antennas have difficulties in receiving the spectrum under 100Hz, we may be better to use a loop antenna which is, electrically speaking, less critical for all reception, but things are not quite that easy.

The 75cm loop antenna described earlier, with its 18 square meters obtained by adding up every single-turn coil surface area, is not good enough to receive signals at lower than 200Hz. To receive signals in the range from 1 to 100Hz we need a 100 times bigger capture area. Because we cannot multiply the number of turns by 100 (in this case we would need almost 10km wire) what we have to do is enlarge the loop size. If we make a 4m by 4m loop with 150 turns, we reach a 2500 square metre capture area, which is enough to push the reception down to the hertz limit. The antenna shown below has a diameter of 1.75metres and it is made with 400 turns of telephone wire (diameter 0.4mm).

This kind of antenna is difficult to construct as a stable structure but it also has a big problem. It is very sensitive to microphonic effect. A light breeze is enough to provoke a 1mm vibration, which can produce strong output signals reproducing mechanical oscillation of the antenna rather than the natural radio signals we want to hear.

Kurt Dietrich's big loop (Octoloop project by Willian Ernest Pine)

To avoid this problem, the antenna should be completely buried in the ground, and because we are using the magnetic component of the signals, this doesn't compromise the reception sensitivity. It is no use burying it horizontally, given that all signals in this band have a vertical polarization.

An even bigger loop, by Hans Michlmayer (Australian). The loop is constructed with 100-pair phone wire and has a diameter of 4 meters.

At its base, the 100 pairs have been soldered one by one in sequence to make a 200 turn coil.

We should bury it vertically in a 5 meter deep ditch ….. a very difficult operation. This project is therefore not suitable for everyone. Considering also that a buried loop is still magnetically coupled to the house electrical wiring, we must remember that such an installation is not entirely free from signal disturbance.

The solenoid antenna

A rather original, though not cheap, solution comes from the use of the solenoid antenna. It works in a similar way to the ferrite rod variety in AM portable receivers, and it is possibility to make a similar product able to receive in ELF and ULF bands.

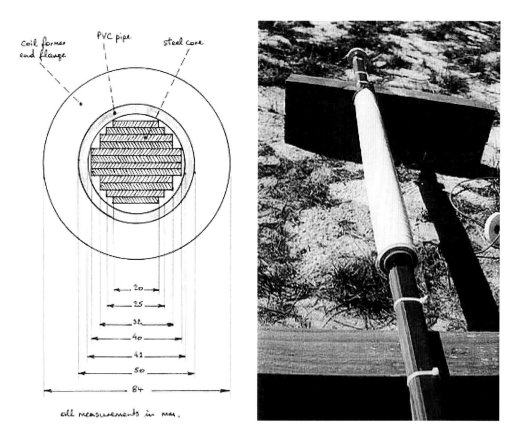

Hans Michlmayer's construction, with core composition made of sheets of magnetic material (steel) and the finished view of the solenoid

131

On a plastic pipe former 1.5m long and 5cm diameter, 70-80,000 turns of copper wire (0.1mm section) is wrapped. We will need in total 8-10kg of enameled copper wire, which we can wrap around the pipe-former by using a lathe to automatically rotate the former, or we can use ready wound spools of 10,000 turns each, mounted on the former and connected in the correct direction to form a single coil unit. The final capture area is not much more than 150 square meter, but the introduction of a steel bar core (previously coated to limit eddy current paths and avoid a "shorted turn" effect) virtually multiplies the number of turns, increasing the antenna sensitivity to very high levels.

The steel bars must be electrically isolated from each other to prevent eddy currents flowing in the core, in the same way as is done for the iron laminations which form a transformer core. The output voltage of this kind of loop does not increase with frequency beyond a few hundred hertz, given that the coil's parasitic capacity makes a signal a short-circuit at higher frequencies. It does guarantee, though, a very good sensitivity even at frequencies under 1Hz, and therefore it is one of the most commonly used antennas for studying geo-magnetic pulsations. Its dimensions, which are not very big, also allow burying it in the ground (after water-proofing treatment) so avoiding vibration problems

H field amplifier

The amplifier connected to the solenoid antenna or to a loop usually has very low impedance, unlike that used to amplify the wire antenna signal. The very practical advantage is that by making the loop work as a current inductor, we obtain an output, which is constant with frequency, and also current amplification devices have a lower output noise

Weak ELF signal amplification is very difficult because of the very high noise in the amplification devices at very low frequencies where most instrument noise is seen. To avoid this we can use techniques where the signal to be amplified is frequency translated into a spectrum region where amplifiers suffer mainly from only a lower level of "white noise". Then at these higher frequencies the signals can be more easily amplified with very little added noise.

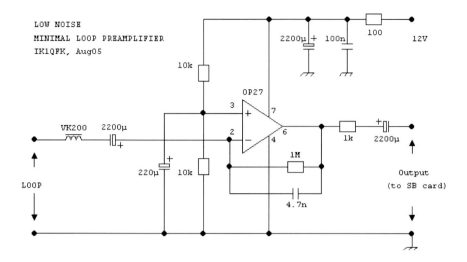

Here an example of a simple amplifier made to work with the signal from the 1 x 1 meter loop consisting of 800 turns of 0.2 mm diameter enameled copper wire. The amplifier, seen from the loop, looks like a short circuit (zero impedance). This kind of configuration, is called "virtual earth". The gain is determined by the ratio between the 1 Mohm resistance and the connected loop impedance.

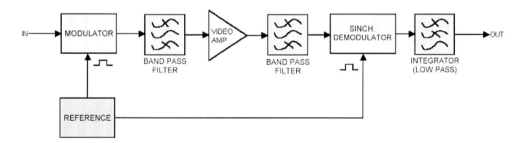

Another technique used for low frequency signal amplification: the chopper-amplifier. With this system we can amplify signals down to DC with very low noise levels (Picture of Andrea Ghedi)

There are also other signal amplification techniques, but we rarely find in them the simplicity of the electric field receivers. Although the inductor doesn't constitute the easiest and most economic way to monitor the 1 to 120Hz band, it does represent the most professional approach. If you need a serious monitoring system working for an extended time, it becomes essential to use a stable system.

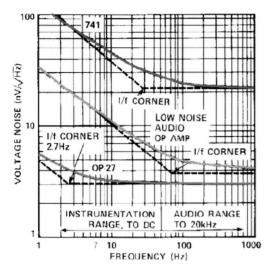

Operational amplifiers are not all the same.

The top line shows the input noise voltage of a µ741, the middle one the plot of a classic low noise audio amplifier, and the bottom line an OP27. At 7Hz the µA741 sounds 20 times more noisy then an OP27.

An electric field receiver constitutes a fast and cheap method, but it is prey to many environmental variables, such as clouds, wind, storms, and rain. When electrically charged cloud starts to rain, the electric field antenna goes crazy, and gives us hours and hours of recording with the background noise at full scale. In the same conditions, an inductor placed or buried a few meters far away, keeps receiving Schumann Resonances normally without being affected by the statically charged rain.

There is a final reason to choose the solenoid antenna. Many natural origin signals at very low frequencies, such as geomagnetic pulsations, originate from the magnetosphere surrounding the Earth. In this case the distance from the point of origin of the signal to where it is received is often less than the wave-length of the signal itself. In this condition, which is called the near-field, the magnetic component is much stronger than the electric component. It can therefore happen that a pulsation is clearly receivable 20dB above the natural hum noise when using the magnetic component, while receiving the associated electrical component we hear nothing apart from the hum noise.

To reproduce this near field condition we can design a very simple experiment where we put a magnetic VLF receiver (like the Easyloop) and an electric receiver (like the RS4) a couple of metres apart. We then adjust the RS4 sensitivity in order to receive natural radio signals, such as statics at the same level as the loop input signal. The two receivers receive just about the same things. Then we position about ten metres further away from the receivers, a petrol engine, such as a car or a lawn mower and we turn the engine on.

The loop will receive the signals at a few hundred hertz radiated by the engine at higher level, perhaps up to 40dB more, in comparison to the electric field receiver. This 100 times increase in signal, referring to voltage, also occurs with geomagnetic pulsations. This is because the source is a magnetic one. The point will be treated in a following chapter which covers radiated and induced fields and signal levels.

Earth dipoles

In many different documents available on the internet, the quoted efficiency of earth probes used as an ELF antenna is very contradictory, and it is hard to properly define the mechanism. Nowhere, in fact, is it clearly explained which component the system receives (electric or magnetic), nor with which polarization, nor what signals it is able to receive. The method is however rather simple so we can make some statements from the results of field experiments.

The "earth dipole" antenna is very simple to construct. Two carpenter's nails in the ground (possibly damp) at least fifty metres apart are enough. Between these two stakes it is possible to observe signals, starting from few hertz up to medium waves. In some situations the European long-wave stations are received better with this system than with a wire antenna. Neglecting here long-wave effects, let us see how the system works in the VLF range.

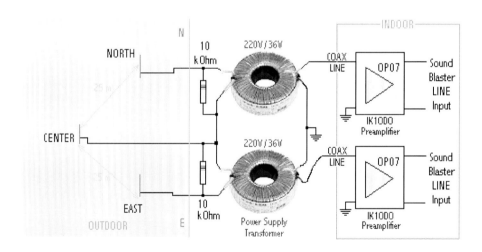

Connection of a pair of earth dipoles to transformers & preamplifiers. The dipoles are placed orthogonally, which permits the signal direction to be deduced, with appropriate software.

To take the signal from between two earth probes we must first interpose, between the antenna and the audio card, some devices physically separating antenna potential and recorder. It is in fact a very bad idea to directly connect an antenna to a computer, because when the first storm comes along, the whole lot will be burned up. A cheap but efficient system relies on using toroidal transformers, similar the ones used in linear power supplies to reduce the supply voltage from 220/110 V to 24 or 12 V.

This way the audio card (or the recorder) is never in physical contact with the antenna, so helping to avoid damage. At the same time the antenna has no mains noise problems and the system does not add more noise apart that already present. A final amplifier allows adjustment of the output level to the input sensitivity of the soundcard. The theoretical reception band of the system goes from 1Hz to around 50kHz depending on the quality of the transformer used.

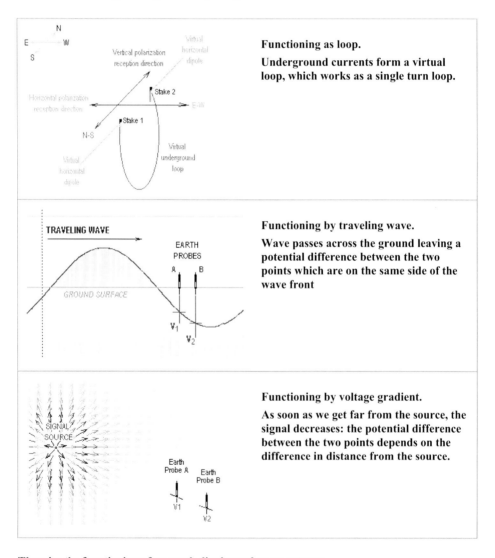

Functioning as loop.

Underground currents form a virtual loop, which works as a single turn loop.

Functioning by traveling wave.

Wave passes across the ground leaving a potential difference between the two points which are on the same side of the wave front

Functioning by voltage gradient.

As soon as we get far from the source, the signal decreases: the potential difference between the two points depends on the difference in distance from the source.

Theories the functioning of an earth dipole used as an antenna.

136

If we don't want to use transformers, another system employs circuits commonly used in measuring systems. Here the measuring device ground reference is modified through the use of a particular configuration of the operational amplifier.

We can formulate some different hypothesis about the functioning of this weird antenna. We could think that the current flowing between the two stakes forms an underground loop and in this case the antenna would be sensitive to the magnetic component of the signal coming from the direction of the line formed by the two stakes. We could also think that the two earth probes act like a horizontal dipole receiving the electric component of the signals arriving perpendicular to the direction of the line crossing the stakes.

Or again, we can hypothesize that the signal is collected simply by the voltage gradient. In other words, it is due to signal level difference, because the two stakes are at a different relative distances from the point of the signal origin. The RF signal, travelling in the ground, would leave a potential difference, collected by the earth probes. In this case the component received would be the electric one and it would be in the direction of the line joining the two stakes.

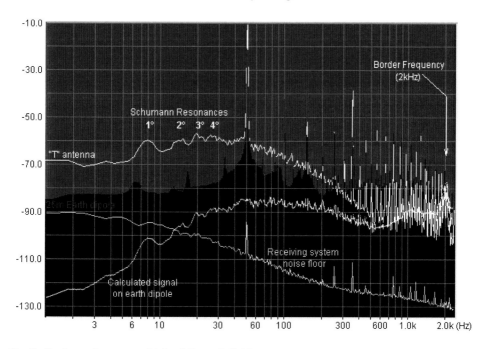

Earth dipole performance obtained through field tests.

From the field trials carried out, it would seem that the magnetic component is the predominant one of the three and it also seems that the effect of other two is almost negligible. The spectrogram obtained with a earth dipole is similar to the one obtained with a vertical loop, oriented the same way as the dipole.

Let's think of the practical aspect and ask "What do we receive?" First of all, a lot of hum noise. If, we are to have a sufficiently "clean" reception with an electric field receiver we must move some dozens of metres from the house. An earth dipole works as well but it must be five times further away from the house..

Apart from this big "detail", that we must install the dipole far from all kinds of electric lines, the antenna is capable of reception on almost all the audio band, starting from 1kHz to 20kHz. It will receive both artificial signals, such as Alpha and military RTTY, and natural origin radio signals such as statics, tweeks and whistlers (if they are present). However under 1kHz the efficiency quickly decreases, and once we arrive in the range of interest, from 1Hz to 100Hz, noises coming from the electric mains, magnetic signals and thermal noise generated by the ground's electro-chemical reactions prevail.

This is not all, the earth dipole has a basically resistive behaviour over the whole audio band (we use it for earth resistance measurements in, for instance, archeology). Going down in frequency, starting from few hertz, the ground starts to show a capacitive behaviour, due to the presence of ions. This effect culminates at around 1Hz, and this is also called "relaxation frequency". When this phenomenon increases, there is a reduction of the received signals.

Despite many sources considering it as ELF "antenna", the earth dipole shows in practice a very weird and ambiguous behaviour. It is not able to receive Schumann Resonances nor the statics usually detectable with a Marconi antenna; at the same time it is also inappropriate in Europe for receiving 82Hz emissions for Russian submarines. Also, for generic listening, or seismic precursor research, there is still a doubt about its real ability to receive frequencies under 100Hz.

17. False ELF and ULF signals

As we have just seen, the ELF and ULF bands have a very large variety of signals, which are very interesting both from a scientific and a strategic way. Even if the message to the submarine will remain unintelligible in its content, it is always fascinating to receive it with home made antennas and receivers. We must, however, be very careful in interpreting the cause of these signals because, even in these bands, as for the phonic signals we have just talked about, it is very easy to be misled.

We can be misled into mistaking simple mechanical antenna vibrations for mysterious emissions coming from ….. "who knows where". We learn, with a little experience how to recognize them so as to avoid false alarms such as of extra terrestrial creatures on a visit or a forecast of earthquakes. Antenna vibrations are a mechanism, which will generate a local signal between 1 and 100Hz, and these signals look like they were received by the antenna, but in reality it is this same antenna which is generating them.

The Capacity Effect on a Marconi antenna

As we just have seen in the chapters about receivers, one of the most simple ways to receive the frequency range from 1 to 100Hz is to use the world's oldest radio antenna, called the "Marconi".

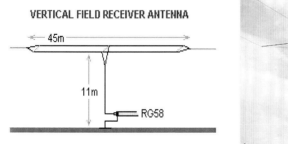

Scheme of a Marconi antenna, with a family of birds perching on it

The Marconi antenna is constructed with simple aerial wires, in different shapes to make up a large capacitance. It is like a huge capacitor with one aerial plate (the wire), and the other being the ground. The electrical structure of such an antenna is identical to a condenser microphone.

In a condenser microphone the foil is vibrated due to the variations in sound pressure, causing a variation of distance between the foil and the fixed grounded plate. If the wire is biased, this capacity variation generates an electrical signal. In the same way a vibrating wire antenna varies its distance from the ground due to wind or birds acting on it, generating an electrical signal, which mimics the vibration. Because of its large dimensions, the mechanical resonance of the antenna is at low frequencies. So vibrations will be much slower than in a microphone, generating signals in 1-100Hz band.

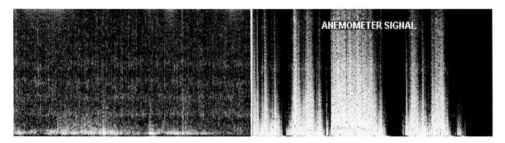

A Spectrogram from 1 to 45Hz showing on the left the ELF band received by the Marconi antenna, and on the right the signal of an anemometer indicating wind presence. The relationship between wind and the increases in noise at very low frequencies is very clear.

Before thinking of monitoring this band, it is wiser to observe what we receive in presence of wind, or when birds use the antenna as a swing, or when someone manually shakes the receiving structure. These simple cases display a wide selection of the kind of signals to be rejected when we analyze what we have received.

Microphone effect in a loop

Even loops, which instead of receiving the electric field are sensitive to the magnetic component of the signals, are not immune from this kind of problem. In this kind on antenna the effect of a generation of fake signal is similar to that which happens in a dynamic microphone.

In a dynamic microphone a membrane is fixed to a coil, which is inserted inside the magnetic field produced by a permanent magnet. The foil movement, which is caused by the sound pressure changes, causes a movement of the coil inside the magnetic field with consequent generation of an electrical signal. A multi turn loop antenna acts in the same way. The fixed magnetic field is provided by the terrestrial magnetic field and a mechanical loop vibration, due to the wind or human factors, produces a signal, which appears with the radiated signals normally received by the antenna.

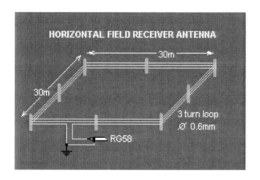
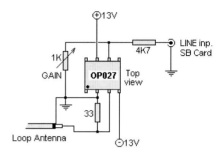

A large horizontal loop antenna and its simple preamplifier using a low noise operational amplifier.

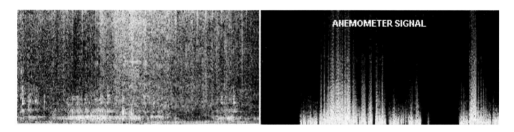

A spectrogram from 1 to 45Hz: on the left what is received by the loop and on the right the anemometer signal revealing wind presence. As for the Marconi antenna, the solar wind induces mechanical vibrations in the loop arms generating fake signals.

We can test the loop using the same procedure used for the Marconi antennas, where wind, mechanical shaking and birds have been used to create a simple signal file, helping us to reject these noises from later reception experiments.

Clothes rubbing, rain and snow effects on Marconi antennas

Returning to the Marconi antenna, we find that even if all structure is rigid, it is sometimes possible to receive wide band noises in the region from 1 to 60Hz, similar to rubbing or a wind sound.

They really are static fields generated by the clothes rubbing on someone walking by the receiving position. If the antenna is a dozen metres high, it is able to sense a very weak static field such as it is described in the Chapter about phonic band signals. Similar traces come also from animals, like dogs, and cats and the intensity of the signal generated is directly proportional to the mass of the animal and to its hair length.

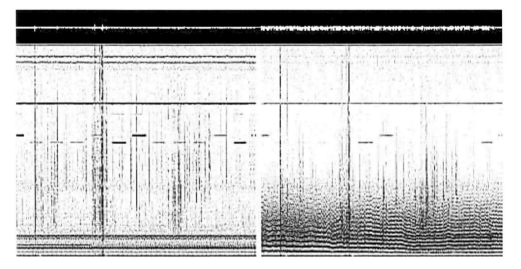

Spectrogram from 0 to 22kHz, recorded during a storm approaching. The left part is recorded with a vertical loop, while the right one is recorded with a T Marconi antenna. The strong voltage, due to static field in the air, induces discharges on the Marconi antenna generating fake signals.

It is much better in this case to make a map of these signals. The solution of fencing around the antennas is not very successful because cats have their own personal concept of their territory. It is perhaps more understandable why the signal monitoring posts of University level observers, are usually placed in the desert or at the poles, and so very far from this kind of disturbance.

Last but not least, is the rain and snow effect on the wire antenna. Snow causes impulsive and deep sounding noises, similar to a finger drumming on a wooden surface, while rain provokes an increasing of the wide band noise, mainly at less than 50Hz. This last phenomenon is due to the effect of the electro-statically charged falling drops.

Metal in motion around loops

Loops are not sensitive to static charges generated by clothing or animal fur. The problem of their response to vibration can usually be solved by burying the antenna, and this way, unless someone jumps on the point where the antenna is buried, every possible kind of mechanical vibration is excluded.

Another hidden trap is revealed by standing within two meters of the antenna and swinging some keys, when we can observe the generation of a signal. Every ferrous object near the antenna deforms the terrestrial magnetic field, and if the object moves, the field deforms varies, and a varying field near a fixed loop produces the same effect as a loop moving mechanically in a stable magnetic field.

The idea of preventing anyone walking close by an antenna or holding keys or other ferrous objects is not easy and is also not sufficient to cure our problems. Even a metallic enclosure produces the same effect (but bigger because of its dimensions), and the same is true for a garden cage made with wire net covered by green plastic. If we install the antenna around the garden, mainly in order to remove it from domestic noise signals, on the first windy day, we will notice on the spectrogram that the band is full of horizontal lines. They are caused by mechanical vibrations of the metallic net, which vibrates under the action of the wind, and just a few millimeters movement is enough to generate an intense signal.

Unless we are owner of a huge Texan ranch, the best thing to do after placing the antenna as far away as possible from any metallic objects, is to manually move some ferrous objects around us and observe the signal that they produce.

18. Static-Field receivers in the SLF band

By static (as in stationary) fields we mean all those signals of very slow variation of under 1Hz frequency. They can be both electric (as fields associated to cloud passage) and magnetic (as geomagnetic pulsations). Once under 1Hz we lose the use of some kinds of antennas and the acquisition systems seen so far, such as the audio card. We will need to equip ourselves in a different way.

The signals we can find, such as geomagnetic pulsations, are of much higher intensity sometimes up to 100 times stronger than Radio Nature signals like whistlers. But the very slow variations make it impossible to use much of the instrumentation described so far.

The wavelengths we are talking about are very long; a 1Hz signal has a 300,000 kilometers wavelength and 1mHz signal up to 300 million kilometers. Reception and propagation of those signals have different characteristics from usual radio signals, and so we must introduce new concepts, mentioned earlier, of the near-field and far-field.

Near-field and far-field

When we receive a signal coming from a transmitter, such an FM radio station, situated few kilometers away, we are in the far-field situation. We could in other words consider the source as a little spot at the horizon. The arriving wave has a regular shape, which means that electric and magnetic field are at right angles to each other, forming a sort of chain transporting the signal far into the surrounding space.

In this situation, either using a whip antenna or a loop, we can recover almost the same signal, because the signal's electric and magnetic components carry the same information. As we move away from the transmitting antenna, the electromagnetic wave decreases in a regular way, in both electric and magnetic components.

However, near to the antenna, in the zone called the near-field, the wave has just been created and has to form into a stable shape in order to propagate into the distance, which we now know as the far-field. In the near-field region, the electric component and the magnetic one are not equivalent and if the source is magnetic, it is the magnetic component that prevails. This becomes much stronger as we get much closer to the antenna.

The zone immediately adjacent to the antenna is called the reactive area and in this region the magnetic signal is many times stronger than the electric one. The region around the antenna where the field is reactive is about one sixth of the wavelength in size. Returning to the FM radio example, this zone extends about half a metre around the antenna. It is clear that no one could think of climbing on the antenna pylon with a radio in his hand to get a better signal, but in the case of very low frequencies fields, the concept starts to have very practical consequences.

We can consider the wave to be completely formed only after travelling a distance equal to the wavelength in use. In the FM case, this would be at three metres away from the antenna. This rule is true only for relatively small antennas, but given that on long waves the antennas always are very small compared to the wavelength, we can consider this rule to be true for all the signals mentioned in this book.

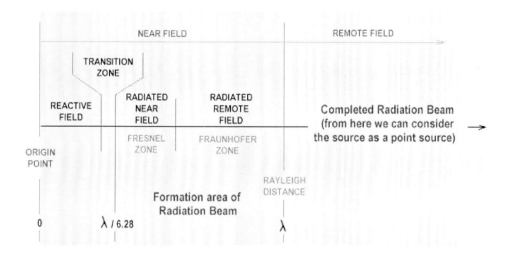

Here is what happens when a signal is created by an antenna or by a natural event. If we consider for instance a 1Hz frequency signal (wave length 300,000km) we will be in the transition region after 48,000 km and we will be in far field after 300,000 km.

Returning to the example of the signals generated by the lawn-mower we mentioned in chapter 15, suppose the engine is working at 1000 revs per minute, we could talk about a field effectively radiated at 1kHz only at a distance of 300 kilometers away! This rule of course is also true for natural signals. For instance, consider a continuous magnetic pulsation of type 2 (PC2), with a frequency of 0.1Hz and a variation period of 10 seconds, then its wavelength is three million kilometers. Its origin is in the terrestrial magnetosphere, on the sun-side, and few kilometers from us in space, so relatively close to us. We are into the reactive field, given that the wave completes its formation three million kilometers away from the start point. That represents eight times the distance between Earth and Moon, to where the far-field starts.

Signals mapping

We have talked so far about strong signals such as military RTTY and about other weak ones like Schumann Resonances, which constitute the natural background noise of our planet between 5 and 50Hz. We have talked about signals used to communicate with submarines and about other ones generated by the solar wind action on our magnetosphere. Some of these signals are seen to be easily receivable, whilst there are others that do not have any magnetic component at all. Before we approach the subject of the reception techniques for static signals, we will summarize all the signals so far listed, comparing the frequency with their signal levels for those signal that are strong enough to receive the signal.

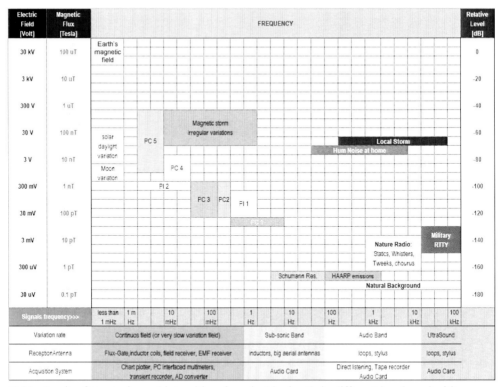

Table showing frequencies and intensities of receivable signals in different bands and with different systems

The table assumes in a general way everything concerning Radio Nature. The first column on the right shows a relative level of signal, assuming as a reference the value of the terrestrial magnetic field. We can observe for instance that the diurnal variation of the magnetic field, compared to its medium value, is around −80dB, in other words 1/10.000 of its mean value. The variation due to the effect of the Moon is even lower.

We can also see that mains harmonics inside an apartment are much higher than Radio Nature signal values, and for this reason we cannot receive whistlers inside our house. In the lower part of the Table, the bands are divided as they have been dealt with in this book and there is also a schematic subdivision of antennas and of the usable receiving systems.

Static Electric Field reception

After all that was said in the preceding paragraphs it would seem useless to measure the electric field at less than 1Hz, given that most of the present signals are received only in their magnetic component. However, a measure of continuous electric component can be used in a different way. As mentioned above, static electric field data will help to protect the receiving station by warning of approaching storms.

A static electric field meter is able to observe when storm clouds with a high electrical charge are thickening above our heads, or better above the sky of the receiving station. The value can change in few minutes from +300V/m (with oscillations usually of some dozens of volts) to −1000V/m, warning us that a lightning discharge is imminent.

We can connect to this system a device capable of switching off all antennas and other apparatus connected, and re-connecting the whole system again when the situation returns to normal. If we decide to monitor for long periods, leaving the PC on to acquire data for a couple of months in summer, this device could become an indispensable aid to the safety of the receiving station.

To receive the electric component at below 1Hz we can use a big T Marconi antenna like the one shown in the chapter about the reception of the signals from 1 to 100Hz. The circuit does not block the passage of continuous current and the reception system works even with static-electric fields. In practice the electric field is so strong that such a big antenna is not really necessary, and a simple 7 metre vertical or a wire antenna of 15 metres works just as well.

A good alternative can be a smaller antenna, but only if we use a receiver with very high input impedance, like the one shown in the following picture with an antenna made of a disk on the top of a whip and forming an air capacitor. The circuit measures the potential difference between the two arms, in other words between the disk and the ground reference.

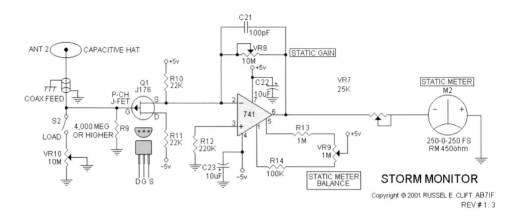

Disk receiver circuit from AB71F, Russel E. Cliff.

Another application for the electric field antenna at less than 1Hz is in the field of seismic precursor research. We believe the system is able to receive the static electrical signal generated during the voltage status preceding the rock breaking. In chapter 15, we saw the circuit from the research paper of Pavia University, which has been operating for many years under the direction of the late Prof. Mognaschi, where a 2.75 meters wire antenna was vertically fixed near to a perimeter wall (just few centimeters away).

The signal was acquired by a high impedance amplifier and by some filters, which suppressed the mains noise at 50Hz. The experiment monitored the signal level variations from few millihertz to 1Hz, allowing a correlation between seismic events and recorded signals, using a paper recorder. The system has been active for only two years (in the seismic research field this is a very short period), but the first results are very encouraging. An impulsive noise, similar to the one observed in the periods preceding the rock shuttering when they are crushed, could be connected to a seismic event

It is strange to observe that at such low frequencies, house walls become transparent allowing reception even inside the building; in the same way, the antenna even works underground. If we take for instance a well (lined with non conductive materials such as a plastic), and insert few meters of insulated wire down it, we can obtain performances similar to that we have with the same length of antenna raised high in the sky.

The disadvantage is the presence of the strong signal at 50/60Hz of the electricity mains, which forces the use of low pass filters with a very steep slope.

Those products are available in the instrumentation and measurement field, but they are rather expensive, and at the same time we must admit are complicated to construct at home with the same performance.

The charge receiver

Another approach to static electric field reception is the "charge receiver". This is not the same as the receiver seen earlier, where the disk antenna is connected to a receiver with very high impedance. In this case the same disk is connected to an amplifier with an input virtually connected to ground. The amplifier collects and amplifies the electric charge in the air through the small current discharging from the disk to the ground.

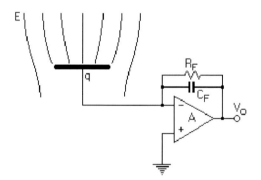

The simple arrangement of a charge amplifier constructed with a single operational amplifier. The amplifier functions as though the inverting pin were ground, as seen by the antenna.

An interesting variant is made by dividing the disk into four sectors and making another disc into a shutter, turned mechanically, so that it alternatively screens two of the four quadrants. The signal, coming from the two static slabs is amplified in a differential mode, obtaining an alternating voltage proportional to the one on the plates.

This frequency translation avoids the annoying problem of amplifier noise at very low frequencies. The detection, after amplification of the signal, is synchronised to the rotational speed of the disk.

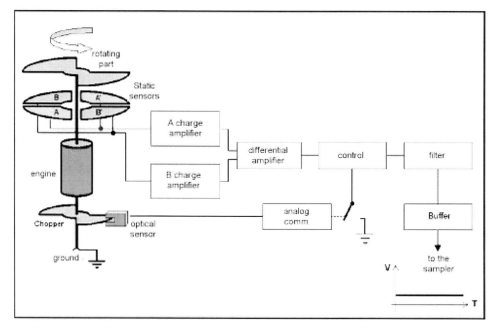

An EMF receiver. The output voltage is strictly related to the electric field value of the sensor (source: Valter Gennaro, Costruzione di un ricevitore EMF, Italy).

It is very interesting to note that, despite the signal to be observed being a static value, no amplifier works on continuous signals, and this is due to the rotary shutter technique. The principle is similar to the one used in professional multi-meters and is called chopping. It is because of this technique that some measuring instruments are able to detect and measure very weak signals, even at such a low level that the instrument noise in the amplifiers would normally prevent this.

The EMF receiver with both the mechanical and the electronic parts visible

It is certainly not a first approach, but it is worth stating that when the field needs to be very accurately measured, and free from all other environmental effects, such as wind and humidity, we must sometimes consider systems more complex than the whip.

Fluxgate magnetometers

The Fluxgate is, since about 1960, the cheapest way of monitoring the intensity of the magnetic terrestrial field. We can buy them on the internet for few dozens of dollars and the most popular amongst them is produced by a British firm called Speake & Co. Ltd. They are constructed on a toroid made of material with a high magnetic permeability, and so an easily become magnetically saturated. Around the ring, which has dimensions under 1 centimeter, is wrapped a coil, like a toroidal transformer. A square wave, internally generated in the sensor box, flows in this coil. It maintains the toroid in saturation during the positive and the negative cycles.

FLUX GATE Magnetometer

Diagram of a Fluxgate magnetometer

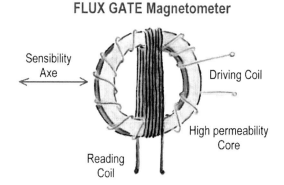

A second coil is wound over the toroid and the first coil, cutting the ring in two equal parts. In the absence of an external magnetic field, the square wave produces the same saturation for both the positive and the negative half-cycles, and the second coil receives regular current pulses. If the device is immersed in a magnetic field, such as the terrestrial one, this balance condition no longer exists, because of the field intensity and its orientation in respect to the second coil.

This unbalance produces a variation of the impulses read by the second coil and so it gives an indication of the magnetic field orientation or of changes in direction of it. The second coil is connected to a voltage-to-frequency converter, which generates a square wave with a cycle depending on the sensor orientation and on the field intensity. This is the signal presented at the device output.

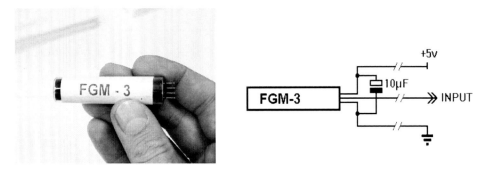

A view showing the size of a Flux-Gate sensor and its simple connections

This kind of device finds application in many activities, from artificial satellites to boats, as an electronic compass, on motorways for the automatic counting of vehicles, to geophysics laboratories for the measurement of magnetic field anomalies and for the solar storm monitoring.

The capsule, which is fed with 5 volts, has a square wave output of variable frequency dependent on sensor alignment with respect to the magnetic field. Its range goes from about 45kHz when is oriented south, to 110kHz when is oriented north. If it is oriented East-West the output value is 75kHz, staying constant as long as the magnetic field is unchanged. A magnetic storm or a strong pulsation provokes a field variation, which causes the sensor signal output frequency to change. We can therefore see that the change in magnetic field frequency-modulates the square wave output from the sensor.

These objects (their functional physics is very clear and widely documented), were also used in the past for pseudo-scientific applications, such as in the Hartmann knobs finding. This theory will be discussed in a following chapter, but, to be clear, we suggest that the phenomenon is not detectable with Flux-Gate or with any of other scientific measuring instrumentation.

The Flux-Gate is very sensitive to mechanical vibrations, like many antennas for low frequencies, and its ideal position is buried 30 centimeters under ground. It must be placed as far as possible from any metallic and ferrous objects, such as for instance a metallic enclosure or from a road crossed by vehicles. Any vibration from these sources can alter the surrounding magnetic field, which will be detected by the sensor. A battery alarm clock, 1 metre away from the sensor, is enough to perturb the magnetic field at a one second cycle, that is at the rhythm of the tiny mechanism inside the clock moving the second hand.

Now we must consider the problem of collecting the data generated by the sensor through its frequency varying square wave. We will reject laboratory systems which use very expensive measuring instruments, so we have two possibilities for exporting our data either as DC signals to send to a paper-plotter, or as signals at a few kHz which we can send to the audio card.

The first solution uses only one integrated circuit, the LM2917, which works as a frequency/voltage converter, and costing only a few dollars, is easily available.

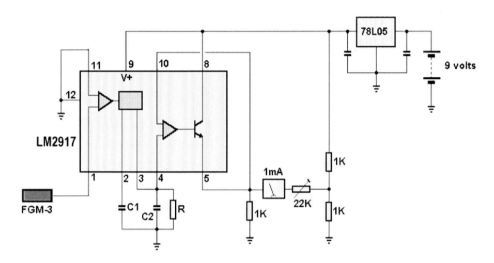

The circuit of a frequency-to-voltage converter. Using a single integrated circuit type LM2917, and few components it is possible to transform the square wave output of the FGM3 into a variable voltage signal. The unmarked components can be adjusted to adapt the level to the recorder, according to the data-sheet instructions.

If it is connected as shown in the picture, the circuit returns a 2.5V level when the input is 75kHz, and when the frequency varies, the voltage level moves proportionally, indicating the magnetic field variation. The output signal can be then connected to a plotter, or to a test-meter with a PC interface for observing and automatic recording of the measurements. We could also add a USB interface device, which are available, often as kits, for few dollars.

Monitoring of the terrestrial magnetic field is now easy to begin. We just have to place the sensor horizontally and turn it until we have an output of 2.5V. At this point the output signal level is calibrated at mid-scale, and any terrestrial magnetic field variation in a positive or negative direction will give rise to an analogous variation about the 2.5V value.

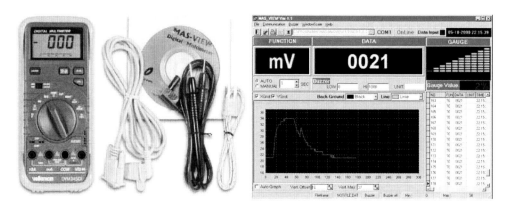

A palm-sized multi-meter with RS-232 interface for recording measurements on the PC. Its cost is below €60 (photo Spin Electronics, Italy. Velleman DVM345Di)

Another system operates by lowering the sensor output frequency through a process called digital-mixing, or heterodyning as shown in the picture, to convert it to the centre of the audio card's frequency range.

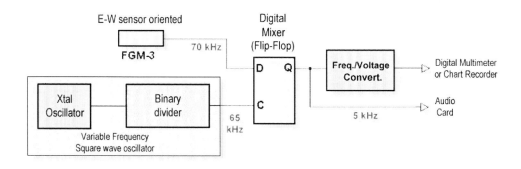

Block diagram of digital-mixer or heterodyne system.

The digital mixer, is achieved electronically with a simple Flip-Flop circuit, which outputs the difference between two input frequencies. If our sensor is generating 70kHz, we just have to set a 65kHz frequency to obtain a square wave output of 5kHz. If the frequency of 65kHz is very stable, the 5kHz output signal carries all the information from the sensor that was in the 70kHz signal.

After some attenuation, the resulting signal can be passed to the line input of the audio card, and using free software such as SpectrumLab (discussed later) we can extract the modulating signal directly from the square wave, so obtaining the magnetic field strength. We can record this on a file and show it on a graph in a similar way to that produced by the plotter.

A sensor like the FGM-3 is able to detect magnetic variations up to some dozens of nT. It is therefore able to observe the stronger geomagnetic pulsations and most solar storms by their effect on the terrestrial magnetic field. Despite its wide reception range of up to 20kHz, this kind of sensor is not able to receive Schumann Resonances because their intensity is far below the threshold sensitivity of this little device.

The solenoid

The solenoid antenna described earlier (the one with 10kg copper and thousands of turns on a high permeability core), is still the most used system for receiving frequencies under 1Hz even if it is not suitable for observing the static magnetic field at 0Hz. Its low frequency cut-off does not usually get under 1mHz

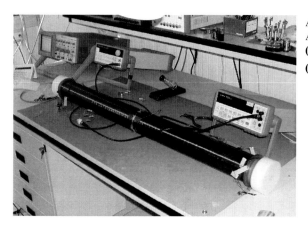

An solenoid for ELF reception made in Astronomic Observatory of Medicina (Italy), CNR

(Photo: J. .Monari).

Except for some specialised antennas such as the SQUID sensors (Superconducting Quantum Interference Devices, constructed of super-conducting material and required to be cooled to a temperature of –250° Celcius with liquid Helium. They are used for instance in submarines.), solenoids are the cheapest and the most sensitive antenna for observing geomagnetic pulsations, including the very weak ones which are not detected by the small but less sensitive FGM-3 sensor.

In this case also the location rules indicated for FGM-3 are still valid. They must be placed far away from the house, far away from electric lines, possibly buried in the ground (after being appropriately water-proofed) and placed as far away as possible from metallic objects, which could move or vibrate. Solenoid antennas are the main sensors used for seismic precursor study at very low frequencies, given their sensitivity and the ease of isolating them from microphonic and mechanical effects by burying them.

Earth dipoles and ELFRAD activities

Another technique for receiving very low frequencies consists on the signal observed between two earth probes, but, as we have seen at higher frequencies, this system has the same limitations, receiving mainly electro-chemical signals originating from electrolytic reactions occurring in the ground.

There is a group who have explored the use of this system quite deeply, using it for radio seismic monitoring. They are known as the ELFRAD (www.elfrad.com). It was founded in 1986 and it is outside any political organization, with the contributions from independent researchers (many of them amateur radio operators). ELFRAD has as its target, the study of the spectrum region from a few dozens of Hz to 1mHz.

The group has developed a system which permits different receiving stations to operate in a similar way, so that it is possible to compare their collected data. One of the targets is to be able to activate a net of receiving systems with at least one monitoring station every thousand square kilometers.

The standard receiving system is composed of an earth dipole a hundred meters long, with a six channel digitizing card (designed by the same group) to transform the signal voltages received into a digital form and support software to permit recording of the collected data on a PC hard disk. The maximum sample rate obtainable is 200 measurements per second and channels not used with the first dipole can be used for a second one, and also for the insertion of signals to provide a precise time reference.

The PC card has also several other functions. It will protect the computer from strong transients in the ground during storms, filtering the mains frequency and separating the computer ground reference from the RF signal ground (earth loop). This latter ensures that the measurement is done in floating mode and the computer does not affect the reading.

The acquisition system is technically competent, but the interpretations on the collected data may be said to be much more audacious. For this reason the organization was bitterly criticized by official scientific institutions and their researchers. The group insists it is able to systematically observe seismic precursors, and their researchers affirm it is sometimes possible to forecast an event few hours in advance.

19. Recording of static fields

The recording of signals, which evolve in a very slow way has always been a delicate matter in many different fields of study: medical, meteorological, and in the laboratory. The technological solutions were first electro-mechanical, but have since developed into electronic digital systems with the advent of the small computer.

The use of paper recorders

The paper recorder is one of the oldest systems for the automatic recording of signals. Before the computer, and even in its early days when large memories were not available at low cost (such as a CD-Rom or a hard disk), one of the most practical systems to compare and store signals was the paper chart-recorder. The working principle is extremely simple. An electric motor or a clockwork mechanism, slowly drags paper from a roll under one or more pens, which are deflected across the paper by external signals, and so mark a continuous trace on the paper indicating the evolution of the signal with time.

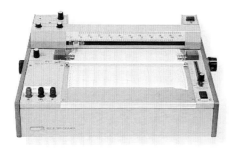

An analogue paper plotter by Radiometer Model REC61

Despite its useful and interesting performance, it is now obsolete compared with a modern PC data logger card.

Photo Spin Electronics, Italy.

The display obtained is immediate and easily interpreted, so that even today many signal logging programs on the PC display the final results like the chart trace marked by the pen. The resolution of a paper recorder can be of a very high level. For example, with a 0.2mm pen writing on a 20cm wide sheet can have resolution of 1000 points, whilst an 8 bit digital sampler gives only 256 points.

The initial cost of these products was very high, for instance, the model shown in the picture bought new, in the 1970s, would have cost as much as a small car. Time passes quickly and the rapid technological development of digital systems made these devices obsolete and of no commercial value. We can now find them in garage sales for just few dollars. The paper plotter systems can still technically useful, for recording signals that have a very slow variation.

The presence of more than one pen can be very useful, making it possible to compare the evolution of several signals simultaneously. Let us suppose we want install a monitoring station for seismic precursors. Then on the four available channels we could for instance connect a small seismograph, a saturation magnetometer, an electric field antenna and perhaps also an earth dipole. The way these instruments respond would be immediately visible marked on the paper, and the presence of a seismic precursor event would become easy to verify.

The main problem of the paper recorders comes when comparing long periods of data recordings. If we use a 30cm long sheet every 24 hours, then in a couple of months we have 18 metres of graph and in a year more than 100 meters. The computer is undoubtedly more practical in this case because it always takes the same space for 1, 10, 100 or 1,000 sheets and it permits a very rapid comparison between sets of collected data.

A second limitation concerns the fact that the display obtained shows how the signals evolve in time but does not permit any easy further processing, such as to derive a frequency spectrum or spectrogram. This has two consequences, first different signals can generate the same kind of information and second the choice of frequency ranges to be analyzed must be decided in advance, with a check only being possible after say a month of data acquisition to determine whether setting needs to be corrected.

With a digitizer on the PC things become much easier, we acquire everything and then we try the different analyses, choosing the one giving the best results. This way we can also decide whether two signals are just similar or whether there is a deeper significance than their mere resemblance.

Recording in FM on tape

This common technique is no longer used, because even here digital electronic technology and the advent of the PC have made this system obsolete, by replacing it with others that are more precise and affordable. It was used a great deal in the past and it is worth recalling how it works, because the principle still has applications in some measuring or signal transfer systems.

As everyone who uses magnetic tapes to record some music knows, it is not possible, with standard devices, to record signals lower than 40Hz, even with chrome or metal tapes. If we want go down under 1Hz, there is no to suitable tape. The FM recording system consisted of translating the continuous current value, to a frequency in the audio band that could be recorded on standard magnetic tape without problem.

The DC signal was set to produce a tone frequency of 3kHz from a generator. In absence of signal (voltage level = 0) the output frequency would be exactly 3kHz, but if the required signal voltage rose then the frequency increased and vice versa. A variable voltage signal ranging from -1 to 1 volt would be transformed into a variable frequency tone from 2kHz to 4kHz, and carrying the same information that was contained in the original signal. A signal from 2 to 4kHz is perfectly compatible with standard magnetic tape, even the lower quality product, and so it was recorded on reels or audio cassette tapes.

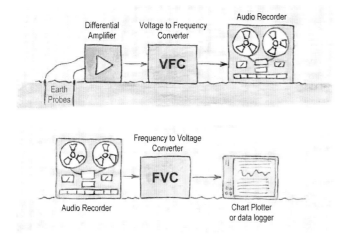

A diagram of an FM tape monitoring system. Several analogue devices are required such as chart and tape recorder just to do the same functions as a simple data logger and a portable PC.

Then the task was to extract the original signal. The tape was replayed and the variable tone from 2 to 4kHz was fed to a device which is the inverse to that used for the modulation operation, a frequency-to-voltage converter (similar to that used to decode the FGM-3 magnetometer signal) recovering, more or less accurately, the original signal.

In a system like this, the quality of the reproduction is governed by several different factors. First is the stability and reproducibility of the tape drive mechanism. A fluctuation in the tape speed will generate a frequency deviation and so a false output signal. If the tape runs at a steady speed, the reproduction will be without any interfering noise.

Another factor is the frequency range that the tape will record. The frequency deviation of the principle signals must be contained within the tape bandwidth limits. A final and critical factor is the quantity of the tape needed. If we use 60 minute audio tapes we would need 24 per day and over a long monitoring period these would be difficult to handle. The maximum reproducible range, even using high quality reel-to-reel recorders is never more than 40dB.

The voltage-to-frequency conversion system is usable even with modern techniques. The signal tone which is FM modulated in the audio band can be directly connected to the PC audio card, where after extracting the original data, the latest results can be displayed in real time, and the earlier data stored to disk, as we saw with FGM-3. This system has the advantage of the paper recorder but we can repeatedly replay the data and try different analysis methods.

PC use: the data logger

In the past, analogue instruments such as tape recorders, paper chart-recorders and plotters were used for recording measurements in every laboratory. Newer technologies have relegated this kind of instrumentation and it has been abandoned as obsolete. The speed of this change is quite shocking. Not many years ago master recordings were put on magnetic tapes and TV external shooting was done with a bulky Betamax "portable video recorder".

This revolution is best summed up with the word we hear all the time, "digital". When used as an adjective it is by now synonymous of quality, though some might disagree. To indicate that a musical product or a video is digital quality means it has high quality technical characteristics. Even in the data recording field, the advent of the digital era has changed the way of thinking. For instance, just as the sound-card replaced the audio tape, the data logger has replaced paper recorders. Basically, data-loggers start from the same concept and they are similar to a sound-card but they are able to record down to DC.

Cards working down to DC are usually of a different type to sound-cards, given that their use is industrial and not the domestic field. They are quite easily available and we can order them over the internet, but they have a disadvantage over sound cards. They are not produced in large quantities, and so they are not as common as sound-cards. The direct consequence of this is their higher price, which can be about ten times the cost of a Sound Blaster.

This kind of digital recorder starting from DC, is called a Data Logger but we can consider it as a test-meter or a multi-meter that will automatically record and file the voltage values it has read. Later, by translating them from tabular format, it can display the results as a graph. Recently, much cheaper devices have been produced, which are more suitable for the non-professional researcher.

The first example shown below has a USB interface, and costing around €40.00, permits simultaneous recording of four channels whilst being powered through the USB connection. It is called PCS10 and is produced by the Belgian firm, Velleman, well known for its high quality electronic kits.

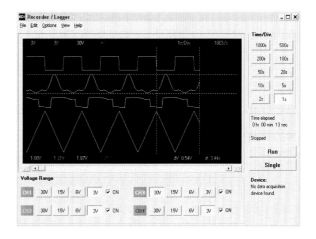

The four channel acquisition system via USB, made by Velleman, and its data acquisitions screen

This device allows a maximum of 100 readings per second (so 50Hz is the maximum frequency that can be captured) to 8 bit resolution (that is 256 discrete levels) and has software provided for data recording on a PC. It is also able to file the collected data in table format, and to display line graphs of the recorded values. This instrument is a very good compromise between performance and price. The product has two limitations, first the resolution at only 8 bits makes it is easy to lose weaker signals, and second the ground terminal, which is common to all the inputs, could generate some difficulties.

A alternative unit is made by Pico Technology, and is produced in two versions, giving either 8 or 12 bit resolution. The cost is around €140.00 for the 8 bit version (ADC-10) and €220,00 for the 12 bit version (ADC-12). These are uni-polar devices with a range from 0 to 5 volts but bipolar versions are also available. The device is powered from the computer provided the correct software is used, and the connection is through the parallel port. It operates up to 20,000 reading per second in the 8 bit version and 15,000 in the 12 bit version. Because many of the more modern PCs no longer have a parallel port for their printer, Pico also produce USB versions of their instruments now. Many of the older parallel port units are appearing, and can be bought cheaply on Internet auctions (eBay) for this reason.

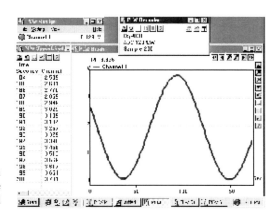

A Pico Technology unit in its 12 bit version and the PC screen which shows the collected data and displays it in graphical form.

The disadvantage over the unit described earlier, comes from the higher price and from the availability of only a single channel. The resolution is however more accurate and the acquisition speed is much faster. Even in this case the product is sold with software able to produce graphs and to file measurements in table format. Pico also produce the ADC-11 in the same price range, which has 11 channels at 10 bits resolution, but is only uni-polar. Newer models offer 12 bits resolution too.

Another product, also from Pico Technology, is ADC-16, costing around €180.00. In this case we have 8 channels sampled more slowly (every 1.5 sec) but with a 16 bit resolution (that is 65,000 levels). If all the channels are not required, channels can be paralleled to increase the sampling rate.

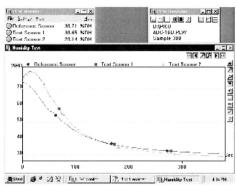

An eight channel high resolution unit by Pico Technology

The very high resolution and so the ability to observe very weak signals make it the interface best suited to semi-professional monitoring. This interface allows constant monitoring so with an electric field receiver and a magnetic field sensor such as FGM-3, it will detect those very weak signals, which could escape the other recording instruments mentioned earlier.

These products can be considered as good substitutes for paper recorders in a simple cost comparison. Consider that a paper recorder uses a paper surface of 20 centimeters, with a writable zone of 18cm. If we have a pen of 0.5 mm we will have a 360 point resolution on the paper, in other words 360 possible levels of signal. In reality it is a bit less than this, due to the mechanical tolerances of the recorder mechanism, let us say certainly 300 points.

If we take as a comparison the cheapest of the products shown, the PCS10, we obtain 256 levels, which is less than the paper recorder but it has four channels. The possibility of setting the graph parameters for a better display and, most important, we have the automatic tabular filing of the values for further study. We could then subsequently obtain curves, a correlation index, a frequency analysis and even spectrograms.

If we extend the comparison to the ADC-16 interface, then to have an equivalent paper recorder, we should have 8 pens and a sheet with a writing area of more than fifty meters. A large lorry would be needed for this task, while with a single interface and a portable PC we can collect a huge quantity of very accurate data even in the middle of a field.

Without doubt paper chart-recorders, which are sometimes incorrectly called plotters, are still very fascinating instruments, mainly for those of us who saw them operating in a technical or scientific application. However, it requires only a few calculations to compare them to the new devices, and to understand that their future is now only in a museum.

20. Yesterday's techniques, today in software

First let us see how we obtained spectrograms with analogue valve instruments in the 1960s. Next we will consider the software available today on the internet, which permits us to pursue more professional style studies. The programs we examine here are capable of very accurate and rather complex analysis, even if we stay in the domain of information technology intended for domestic use. Perhaps at first they could seem to be a bit difficult, and full of unfamiliar terms (certainly Spectran or Spectrogram shown in chapter 9 are), but when we look deeper they can be seen as indispensable instruments.

The FFT in the past

Looking to the past we see how spectrograms were first done in the 1960s, when, with the beginning of the atomic era and the cold war, many resources were concentrated on VLF.

Those times were the era of vacuum tubes, also known as valves, then systems were nothing like the easy to use portable computer. The size and costs of these devices were important so that only a few models were constructed mainly for military laboratories or university research centres.

One technique that was used consisted of putting the recording to be analysed (perhaps about a couple of seconds in length) on a magnetic tape running in a loop. Then a replay head, like the ones used today in a cassette recorder, would repeatedly read the same signal. With each successive passage the recrding was passed through a 40Hz wide band-pass filter, which was tuned each time to a different centre frequency.

The output signal from the filter controlled a printer, which, line by line, plotted the spectrogram with a frequency resolution of 45Hz and a time resolution of 10ms. To obtain the spectrogram, five minutes of processing were needed. The system produced by Kay Electric was called a "Sonograph" and it was able to analyse signals in the range from 85 to 8000Hz.

Another technique, by Raytheon, incorporated in a device called "Rayspan", utilized a single pass of the recording and produced the spectrogram in real time. The reading head to do this was connected to 420 valve filter circuits in parallel, each one tuned on a different frequency. The outputs of these filters were scanned at high speed by a switching device with the output voltages driving the monitoring printer. The power consumption of this equipment was extremely high and the spectrogram was reproduced on a paper strip only 3.5cm wide. The system was usable from 50Hz to 50kHz with a frequency resolution of 32Hz and a time resolution of 10 milliseconds.

Today a common sound-card permits this analysis to be accomplished in real time, with a practically a unlimited quantity of data storage. The filtering is achieved in real time, we can display the FFT in a colour palette with a frequency resolution a thousands times better, and a time resolution 500 times better, for a full frequency range from 1Hz to 24 or 48kHz (depending on the soundcard). All of this can be achieved today in a device little bigger than a cigarette packet, weighing few dozen grams, with very low power consumption and costing only €50.

If we take just a moment to think of the potential of the systems we have today, it is not that difficult to see that scientific research of this kind is really affordable to anyone. The problem is that the soundcard alone is not enough, and some software is needed to manage it and to initiate all the operations we have listed. In the following paragraphs we will describe some software even more complex than the ones cited so far. The time necessary to learn how to use them is longer than that for the programs described in the Chapter 9, but the improved performances compensates for our efforts.

SpectrumLab

In SpectrumLab we have just about the most complete free program for real-time signal analysis. The author is a German amateur radio operator DL4YHF, his name is Wofgang Buscher, and he releases a new version just about every month, adding to the previous one the suggestions for facilities he receives from users.

The program is not that simple to use since, on top of a classical spectrogram generator core, it implements a huge quantity of functions developed at different times. The result is a spaghetti type software (a term used to distinguish this product from ones fully planned in advance) and it has to be deeply studied before use. The author has however covered every function with a new chapter of the user's guide, which is provided together with the program. This book is already over 150 pages and it has become a real treatise on signal analysis.

SpectrumLab is able to manage all VLF monitoring phases automatically, starting from saving the spectrogram image, to the wave files of the signals, and ending up with decimated wave (described later on) in order to save space on the hard disk. We just have to instruct the program how to proceed and then the station records without our presence.

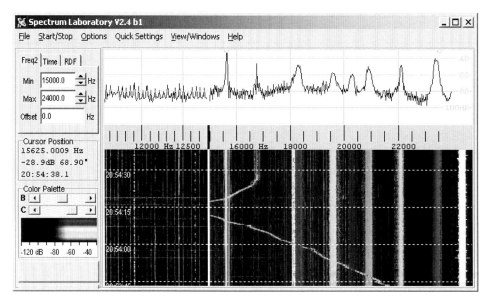

A SpectrumLab screen shot. We can see the spectrum in the upper white part and the directional spectrogram in the lower part. The colour spectrogram also gives information about direction of arrival of the signals.

The program permits the stereophonic visualization of the spectrum, of the spectrogram and of the signal amplitude. It even works as a digital oscilloscope, as a phase meter, as function and noise generator and as a plotter with up to 20 channels. It also has the facility, on every one of the 20 tracks, any kind of measurement of an input signal, ranging from the wide band noise to a single signal, and from the frequency to the average value of the noise in a given frequency interval.

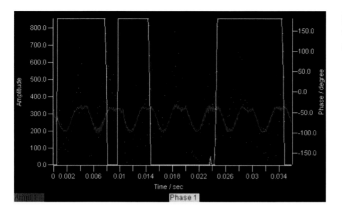

Screen shot of SpectrumLab, when used as a dual channel oscilloscope

The function making it unique is the incorporated mixer which, once the program has started, replaces the Windows mixer.

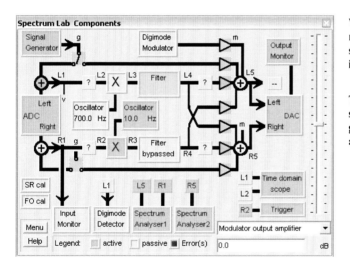

With the SpectrumLab mixer we can manage our sound-card as it was a small instrumentation laboratory

The sound-card becomes a spectrum analyzer, a signal generator and a filter system, all at the same time.

We can easily visualize the different functions of the sound-card as though they were single boxes, controllable in a simple and independent way, also allowing real time application of filters to the signal.

It is possible, for example, to insert a signal, to add a frequency reference given by an internal generator, to filter it from harmonics with a "comb filter", to convert it in frequency, to display the input on a spectrogram and on the output, to automatically record the signals in wave format and simultaneously to display a plot of the interesting values. All this can be done in real time, whereas to reproduce the same functions in the audio band, and with traditional instruments, we would require a huge stack of electronic instrumentation.

167

Besides the decoding of some coded signals, such as "Digimodes", this software also allows for the connection of two antennas for RDF (Radio Direction Finding) operation, which permits the arrival bearing (azimuth) of a signal to be found without moving the receiving antennas. More detail on this function later.

The program is able to execute all these operations either on signals at the sound-card input, or on a stored wave-format file, which was previously recorded or perhaps acquired by other sources.

Cool Edit

Cool Edit is the program preferred by audio amateurs, because it is one of the most practical instruments for doing audio editing. Its main function is handling and modifying wave files, or creating new ones through the simultaneous management of many audio tracks, just as it happens in recording studios.

The multi track facility is not that interesting for us, but effects such as delay, equalization and sampling rate change can be very useful in processing already recorded files to clean noises from them. The program is useful both for recording and for reproducing, but to apply the facilities we must work directly on a wave file, on which we have previously recorded the signal we wish to modify.

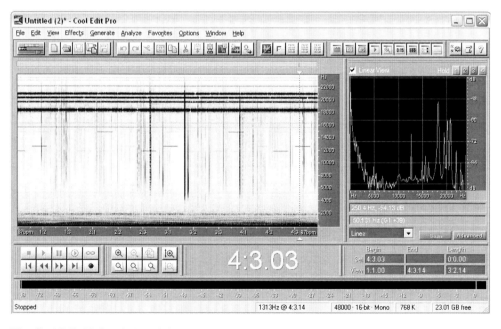

The Cool Edit Main window: it is very accurate and the functions are very easy to use, even for beginners.

The program, despite its complex displays, is simple to use because it has been set-up like a traditional recorder. The oscillograms, spectrums, and spectrograms are displayed at high quality and it allows the operator to skip quickly from point to point, even in very long files, zooming in to see the detail.

The program was created by Syntrillium, in the mid-1990s, and rapidly became very popular with music lovers. In 2004 Adobe acquired the product from Syntrillium, becoming a dealer and changing the program name to "Audition". The software is available from Internet program main distribution portals. The license is now commercial (it costs around $300) but the trial version is free.

SpectraLab

This one is a Shareware program from America, created by Sound Technology (www.soundtechnology.com). While Cool Edit was conceived for those who wanted to make music, SpectraLab is for those who are more attracted to studying and understanding the function and use of acoustic loudspeakers, rather than using them for listening to music. It is a good laboratory tool to make tests in the audio band, and only requires the use of sound-cards as the testing device.

This program allows analysis both in real time and on previously recorded files. It works as a recorder but it does not permit the planning of the operations as does SpectrumLab , because it has not been designed for this kind of application.

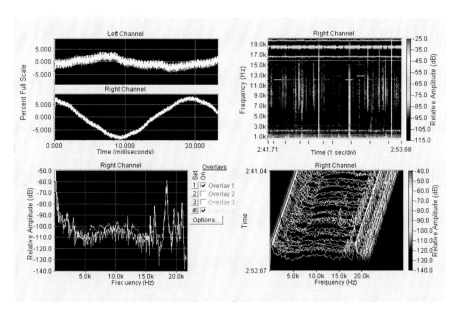

SpectrumLab screen shot with the main function displays done by the software oscillogram, spectrogram, spectrum and three-dimensional spectrogram.

Besides the classical spectrograms, spectrum and oscillograms, we can display the addition or subtraction of signals in the channels. The sound-card output can also be used as a generator of noise or of signal, and can be used to investigate the performance of say an amplifier. One of the two input channels is applied to the amplifier input where the generated signal from the sound-card output has also been connected and the other input is connected to monitor the output of the amplifier. This allows us to obtain a curve of the frequency response of the amplifier, or of a signal receiver or a loudspeaker connected to a HI-FI. Although SpectrumLab has all the facilities for this kind of operation, it is a bit more complicated to use.

21. Unattended operation

The approach over the last ten years of research activity has changed greatly, due to the support that information technology has given to us, we now have many different ways of working available to us compared with the traditional pattern.

We just have to think the field of data processing, where in the 1980s there were huge numbers of people engaged in frantic activity supporting devices with endless tables full of numbers coming out of printers with as many colored lights as a Christmas tree. Today a single data analysis centre manages data thousands times bigger and it operates automatically with calculators communicating with them and out towards the whole world, all without human presence.

Another example comes from FM radio stations, which since their birth were places for meeting to exchange ideas and they had a continuous flow of new people. Today many of them are a simple computer server with a hard disk full of MP3 songs, with a software program automatically playing the tracks and inscrting advertising material with high precision.

Amateur radio and research activities have themselves been involved in this whirlwind. The way for a European in the 1990s to listen to a South American radio station was by losing a night's sleep, turning the tuning knob and hoping that the signal would be favorable this time. If conditions were not good enough, the listening was postponed. Nowadays the SDR (Software Defined Radio) receiver and computer are part of the system, so that activities can be easily planned beforehand, automated, and the listening can be done subsequently, with plenty of time and in a relaxed manner.

Certainly automation has taken away much of the charm of the radio explorer's activity, but from the another view, we are now able to undertake non-stop research projects, in a short time and with very cheap instruments. The natural-origin radio signal field is a classic example where we are no longer forced to lose a night's sleep looking for whistlers, out in the garden to avoid all the problems of mains noises. Today it is possible to plan to leave a receiver operating and connected to a computer to automatically record at specific times and obtain the same or better results. This can be achieved in a number of different ways as we will see below.

PCM recording: auto wave

Certainly the simplest way of recording the audio signal coming from the receiver is directly through the sound-card. The large high performance hard-drives, which are installed on every computer today, make it possible to record for an entire day.

If, for instance we need to monitor the Radio Nature scenery during an eclipse of the moon, we just need to set the computer to record and write a wave file for the four hours in the middle of the event.

The same procedure can be used if, for instance, we need to analyse what happens during a solar storm. We can always analyse the collected data in detail later. The most interesting acquisitions can be saved and filed in a permanent archive, while all the rest of the recordings can be erased to make room for more new files. We can organize a signal gallery with little effort, filed by type, listening band, date, hour of the reception. An archive like this, done in traditional way on tapes, would have taken years of work to complete.

There are several appropriate programs for this kind of activity, and we will just mention two of them. The first one is NCH Timer: this software is free for evaluation or personal use only. It is downloadable from http://www.world-voices.com/software/nchtimer.html. It permits the planning of multiple recordings at different times, and allows daily recordings always starting at the same time, and it is possible in this case to fix the duration of the recording.

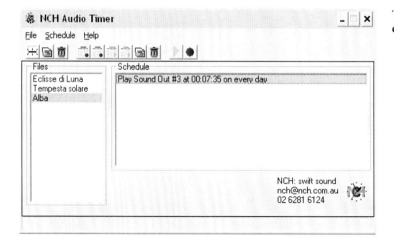

The very simple, basic console of NCH Timer

The program is very simple to use, and for operations such as coordinated listening between different operators in different locations, this is a good, fast and cheap solution without the necessity of reading a user's manual for hours.

Even SpectrumLab, which was summarised in a preceding chapter, is suitable for unattended operations, allowing many options in save or capture mode. Recording can be planned in a table by choosing either to do the acquisition in the regular way or with different times and durations.

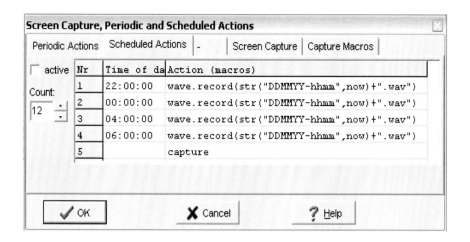

The SpectrumLab recording table. This should not be used without first reading the user instructions; it has no programming limits. At first it can seem a little daunting, but then, once we are used to it, it is very easy to work with.

SpectrumLab has no limits in its data saving mode. For example files can be saved as "garden_date-hour.wav" indicating automatically the place, date, and time when they are saved. An archive of data built in this way is very easy to consult. Let us suppose we want to analyze an audio spectrum corresponding to a local earthquake. We will want to find just the files with the date and time of an event, and to verify if the seismic activity produced any radio signals.

Certainly this program is less straight-forward to use than the preceding one, but the user's guide (in English) with it, explains all the options in a very concise way. SpectrumLab also accepts automatic start-up modes, where in the case of a power failure during a non-stop monitoring, the program restarts again as soon as the situation is back to normal.

The ability to be able to program recordings is very helpful during synchronised listening sessions. If the reception from the house is possible, we can easily plan it in advance, and so avoid having to wake up very early to start the session. At the programmed time the computer turns on, it acquires the spectrograms and then it automatically files them, and at the desired time it turns off, so the operator can analyze the collected data at his leisure.

So, we see that synchronised listening sessions are possible, and the collected data can be reliably compared with that collected by other researchers. It would be crazy to try to manually synchronise monitoring sessions of, say, the first five minutes of every hour, on an entire week end, but if it were programmed on a computer it would only take up some free space on your hard disk.

Automatic image saving

We will now look at other information resources which have changed the way of thinking about and operating a radio. We now have the facility to automatically save spectrograms whilst the signal is being analysed on the screen, with in many cases equally as good a result as if the human operator were present.

If the signals being observed are, for instance, slowly evolving such as Schumann Resonances, we need to make the spectrogram run slowly, saving a screen every 30 minutes. Then with a small collection of just fifty images saved automatically, we have for analysis a record of the whole spectrum region per day, or per month or even per year.

There are many ways to automatically save spectrogram images. We can for instance use three single programs, one for spectrograms (eg Spectrogram), one for showing date and hour (eg "Title Time" http://www.rsoft-home.de) and one for automatically saving the display window (eg "2020" www.hotfreeware.com).

In this way, for example, we would have the automatic saving of the Spectrogram display with a title, date, and hour of the operation as files, which we can then name with numbers or meaningful file-names.

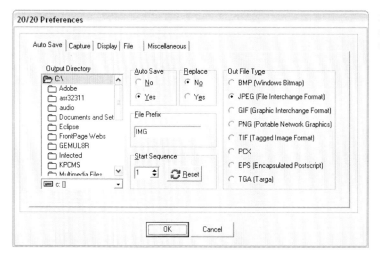

2020 setup screen shot - quick and simple to operate

Another alternative is the direct use of photo-retouch programs. Many of them have an automatic "screen capture" function, like for instance "Paint Shop Pro" (see www.corel.com, www.tucows.com or www.download.com), but they a bit more complicated compared to the first solution, because they don't usually save the data on a file, but they open a new window for each screen captured, and so we have to periodically enter the program and save the open image frames one by one, naming them as we proceed.

A further possibility is to use programs for the spectrograms, which already include the automatic save option. The simplest to operate amongst them is "Spectran" (www.weaksignals.com). Here the screen shows the date and time of saving and also the time markers (ticks), which can help accurately identify events which occurred during that screen display.

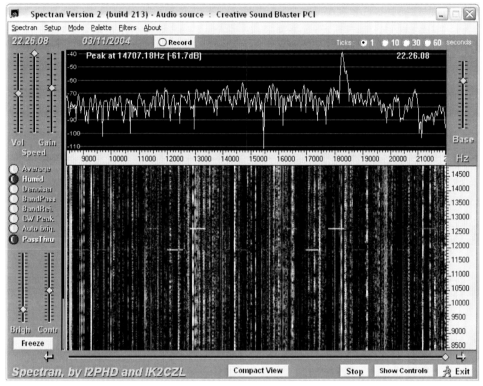

A Spectran screen saved automatically. The saved image includes the time at the instant of saving, and the date and time markers.

For those who are already familiar with these operations, we can suggest you try "SpectrumLab". The program permits image saving in files like the audio files, and the files can be automatically named with date and hour of the saving, to make it easier to locate the material we are searching for later.

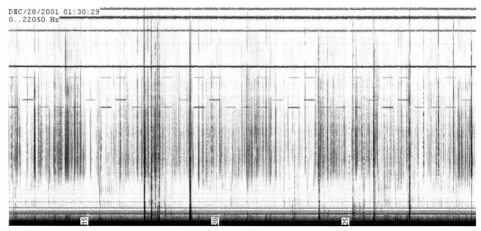

20 second wide band reception saved by SpectrumLab

In the picture is an example of 20 seconds of spectrogram acquired with SpectrumLab in the frequency range from 0 to 22050Hz. The program automatically labels the pictures to be saved inside the image, indicating date and time of the saving, the frequency range and the time scale. All the parameters can be varied according to our needs.

Under-sampling

When buying the very expensive professional acquisition cards, it is possible to choose the sample rate, which is the number of times per second the signal is measured and consequentially also the pass-band. In the more common cheap sound-cards, this is not possible. In PC sound-cards the sample-rate values allowed are usually 5512, 11025, 22050, 44100 samples per second, corresponding respectively to an audio pass-band of 2756, 5512, 11025 and 22050Hz (the pass-band in Hz is obtained by dividing the sample rate in half).

If our interest is concentrated on particularly low frequency bands, for instance under 100Hz, we are forced to waste much space in recording it on the hard disk, because the minimum band pass allowed is 2756Hz, taking up 250 times more disc space than is really necessary for our requirements.

The solution to this problem comes from a process called under-sampling or signal decimation. The sound-card in this case is over-ridden, the signal enters the input port and is sampled at a standard speed allowed by the hardware.

Before being recorded on the hard disk the computer decimates the collected samples, notably decreasing the number of data samples to be recorded and therefore even the frequency pass-band to be saved. This process can be done in automatically and the final result is identical to a card, which actually samples at the lower speed.

Let us suppose for instance we record our signals with a sampling rate of 11025 and therefore with a 5512Hz pass-band. Then in barely 60 seconds of stereo recording we will have filled 2.5MB (2,500kilobytes) of disc space.

If our interest is confined to the lowest part of the spectrum, such as on S.R., seismic precursors or direct transmissions to submarines, we can record our file at a lower sampling rate, so occupying much less space on the disc. If we are content with a 230S/sec sampling rate (that is a 115Hz bandwidth), then for the same recording we would have filled only 60kB of disc space.

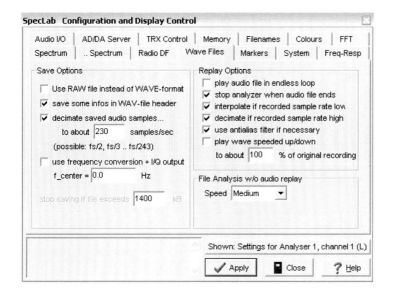

Control panel screen shot showing saving a decimated wave with SpectrumLab.

A continuous recording of monitoring data for 24 hours a day from 0 to 120Hz for 15 days and stored as wave files can easily be fitted on a single CD-Rom. The recording function for decimating the files is available in the SpectrumLab software.

The same software, with appropriate control settings, permits us to choose both the band-pass range and also the preferred frequency interval. We can therefore record automatically the band from 1 to 100Hz, or else the portion going from 6150 to 6250Hz according to the phenomenon we wish to study.

If we use a sound-card it is essential that the main acquisition employs one of the sample rates expected by the manufacturer. Some software such as CoolEdit can force a different sampling rate, but this way the sampler does not work properly, and this results in decreased input sensitivity and the generation of false signals. Only a process such as the one used by SpectrumLab results in effective under-sampling without loss of signal quality.

Plotting and correlations

Another interesting facility, available during automatic monitoring or through the processing of a previously saved wave file, is the plotting function. The spectrogram is an extraordinary way of identifying weak signals buried by noise, but it can also have some limitations when we need to compare how some values vary in intensity over very long periods.

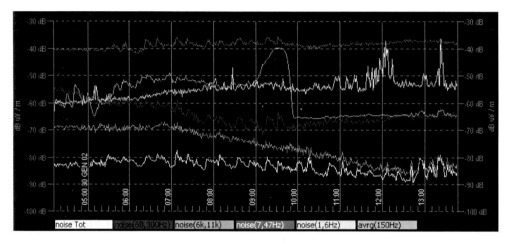

A plot function obtained with SpectrumLab (on screen the traces are colored). This example shows a comparison over 10 hours of the following levels: total noise from 1Hz to 11kHz, noise from 60 to 300Hz, noise from 6 to 11kHz (the typical zone for static in stormy weather), noise from 7 to 47Hz, noise at very low frequencies and finally the average value of the third mains harmonic

Many studies of seismic precursors indicate, in just this way, the possibility of perceiving electric signals, which could perhaps forecast a earthquake. Even this kind of display is available with SpectrumLab software, where the graphics display allows us to keep tabs on 20 items at a time. For each of these, it is possible to decide the frequency interval and the type of item to plot (level, noise, frequency, etc).

The finalised graph can be saved automatically as an image or it can be exported as a text file, to be read into other programs such as Excel for further processing and/or analysis. A cross comparison of the plot with the spectrogram allows us to exclude from our research, all signals with a recognisable origin, like, for instance, those generated by the wind vibrating the wire antenna arms and provoking a microphonic effect.

This software is freeware, the receiver is very simple, and the acquisition sound-card is very cheap, the PC is in everyone's home…. But the range of possible data is huge. Once studies like these, in times when we would have used a paper recorder and magnetic tape FFT analysers, would have required a very large capital investment. Nowadays we can do all this at home and perhaps the recording, forecasting an earthquake, is already stored on the hard disk of some researcher. We just have to find the best key to the interpretation.

From data recording to wave file

Plotting and spectrogram functions are not only available for recorded wave files. If, for instance, we use a different acquisition system from the sound-card, such as a digital multi-meter, we find the final data consists of a table of numbers corresponding to the values read by the meter.

If we use for example a three-digit multi-meter, it is possible to relate the value to an 8 bit sampler, which will return a number from 1 to 256, according to the value read. Even in this case we can handle the data as if it were a wave file and so we can perform all operations we have seen so far. The sound-card does exactly the same job, it converts the analogue value of an input voltage into a number from 1 to 256, in case of 8 bit sampling, and from 1 to 65536 in case of 16 bit sampling.

To do a series of data analysis, in the same way as we do for wave files, we have two requirements. First the program used must accept its input data in text format. Two programs that have this capability are Cool Edit and SpectrumLab.

The second requirement is that readings of collected data must be presented in a certain form. We can use any program, which allows the final saving in TXT, such as Word, Excel, or even Windows Notepad. The file must be re-compiled in the following way. At the beginning of the file, we must indicate the number of readings in the file, the sampling size (8-bit or 16 bit), the number of channel (1 for mono or 2 for stereo), and the number of readings per second (sample rate), followed by one or two columns with data.

This is the way we tell the program that the file we are opening is composed of 745 readings, obtained with a 8 bit sampler (so with values lie between 1 and 256) which are in pairs (stereo) and that samples have been taken at a 200 per second rate. We now just have to save the file with a name like measures.txt and we open it with SpectrumLab or CoolEdit.

An example of the start of a file might be:

```
SAMPLES:          745
BITSPERSAMPLE:    8
CHANNELS:         2
SAMPLERATE:   200
117     132
133     164
123     109
116     139
142     110
```

….and so on for other 740 lines.

The file will be managed exactly as if it were an original wave one, in fact closing the program we will be asked if we want to save it, and we can now choose to save it as simple text file (by choosing ASCII TEXT DATA format) or as wave file, like a normal audio file. CoolEdit also allows the inverse function, making it possible to move from a wave file to a text file, which clearly tabulates all the data.

This procedure also explains some detail about files saved in wave format. They are basically just a list of measured values, starting with some identification lines describing the file content (this part is called "header") and indicating length and kind of sampling used.

22. *Managing FFT parameters*

The Fast Fourier Transform, most often referred to by the initials FFT, is a process for obtaining the frequency spectrum of a signal and its relative spectrograms. Jean Baptiste Fourier was an important French mathematician and, in his book in 1882 *Théorie analitique de la chaleur*, he theorized that complex mathematical functions can be split up into sums of other simpler functions, namely sines and cosines. In those times there was no radio or computers and the mathematician had this brilliant intuition at a theoretical level of mathematics "only".

Certainly he did not imagine that, after a hundred years, this principle would be one of the most important theories used in signal analysis. To demonstrate the concept with a practical example we can show that a signal, even though complex and chaotic, can be broken down into a series of simpler signals, of which it was originally made up. The summation of these simple signals regenerates the original signal. This can allow us to find and isolate very weak signals hidden in a lot of noise or disturbed by other interfering signals.

To cover this important subject, in full, would require a lengthy treatise, and it would be necessary to introduce some very complex concepts, such as negative frequencies and conjugate complex signals. This is not the right place for explanation of these topics, because we only need to understand the significance of the result of the process. So we will just talk about the basic principles, trying to simplify the subject matter. The target of this chapter is to give a short guide, so that a user can understand the significance of the parameters needed to set up programs like SpectrumLab and Spectrogram.

FFT formulas

In this chapter we will refer to a very few simplified formulas, and only those which can be useful to set up different software for the generation of spectrograms. In fact, whilst it is clear that by changing the number of FFT points in the program, we change the spectrogram, it is not easy to see why this happens.

To understand this, we can go back to look at the commonest way we display a signal, as a graph of amplitude against time, like the trace we can see on an oscilloscope screen, also called an oscillogram.

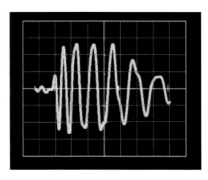 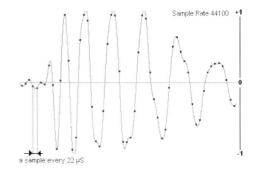

A time varying signal as shown on the screen of an oscilloscope and (right) the same thing displayed on a PC through audio card sampling

The signal amplitude varies in time and the trace shows its representation. If we specify a predefined time interval, for instance one second, we can analyze the spectrum of the signal for that period. We can calculate the single frequencies of which it is composed and their amplitudes, giving us the power spectrum curve, which we would see on a spectrum analyzer screen.

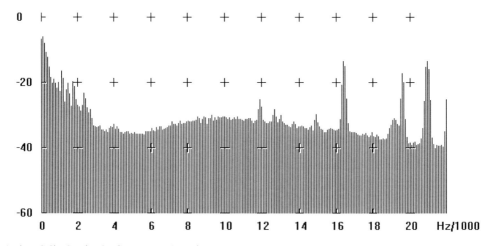

A signal display in the frequency domain

The sum of the single frequencies represented by the bars returns the original signal of the oscillogram. We have, in this way, the FFT of one second of signal.

If we continue making a spectrum analysis every second, we will obtain a sequence of curves showing us how the spectrum varies as time goes by.

182

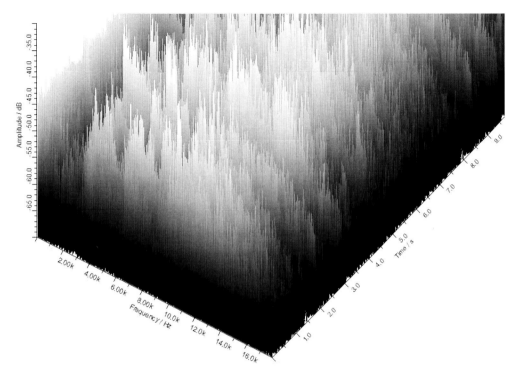

A 3D spectrogram, also called waterfall display

This kind of display is called 3D (three-dimensional) spectrogram. Really, even if it is very colourful, it is difficult to interpret. It is better to make a two dimensional picture with the data, like the spectrogram shown in the book.

The spectrum and spectrogram calculation is based upon the quantity of bars chosen during the analysis, and therefore, upon the quantity of individual points used in the analysis. This number is also referred to as the "FFT memory" or "FFT buffer". The relationship linking the bars and the FFT points is:

Number of Spectrum bars = Number of FTT Points / 2

If we chose in the analysis program a 1024 Point FFT, we will get 512 spectrum bars.

Time resolution, frequency resolution & FFT gain

The number of FTT points also defines the frequency resolution, which indicates how many hertz are represented in a single bar (in other words, how large the "filter" of each bar is). The FTT bar, which is similar to the control on a hi-fi stereo graphic equaliser, is also called "FFT bin", to emphasize that it contains the energy in a small frequency interval and not of a single signal. The relationship between frequency resolution and the number of FFT points (or bars) is:

Frequency resolution = Frequency span / number of bars

If our spectrum represents the range between 0 to 22050Hz and it is composed of 512 bars, each one of them will be about 43Hz wide. As we saw, the frequency interval depends on the sampling number, according to the formula:

Maximum frequency that can be represented = Sample Rate / 2

Then, we can see that:

Frequency resolution = Sample Rate / number of FFT points

If, for instance, we choose in the program a Sample Rate of 44100 Sample/sec and a FFT of 1024 FFT points, we will obtain a frequency resolution of 44Hz (that is each bar will be 44Hz wide). From here, we can assume that the more points we select, the more bars we will obtain and so the frequency resolution will be higher. This means a greater possibility of recognizing weak signals in the noise because we know that the narrower the channel (the bar width) the lower is the noise power. Frequency resolution data is sometimes indicated in the software, and it is automatically calculated during the FFT point choice.

The advantage gained by increased frequency resolution, causes the resolution in time to decrease, because an FFT made of many points takes more time to collect and so it is less able to distinguish short period signals. This does not depend on the computer speed but is a fixed parameter of the FFT. Resolution in time and frequency definition are inextricably related, so that if one of them increases, the other one automatically decreases, and vice versa. The relationship for this concept is:

Time resolution = 1 / Frequency resolution

Or, if we want to express the concept in FFT program language, we can talk about the time to fill the FFT temporary buffer, that is the minimum time required to acquire the necessary points to make the required FFT calculation.

Buffer filling time = 1 / Freq. resolution = FFT points / Sample Rate

This is the reason why 82 and 76Hz transmissions for submerged submarines are very very slow. The signal is very weak and it is drowned in noise, and it is necessary to use a very high resolution in frequency to receive it, therefore the transmission of information must be very slow. A quickly transmitted signal would just not be received. Let us take another practical example: we set on a SpectrumLab screen shot (or on anyone else's FFT program) a 5512Hz Sample Rate and a 16384 FFT point number. The resolution in frequency will then be 0.336Hz and the resolution in time will be 2.97 secs. In practical terms, if we receive a 1000Hz signal, we will only be able to see it on the spectrogram if it lasts for at least three seconds. If the signal we receive is a normal speed telegraphy transmission, we will not be able to distinguish the dots and dashes on the spectrogram, but we will see a continuous line going up and down in intensity.

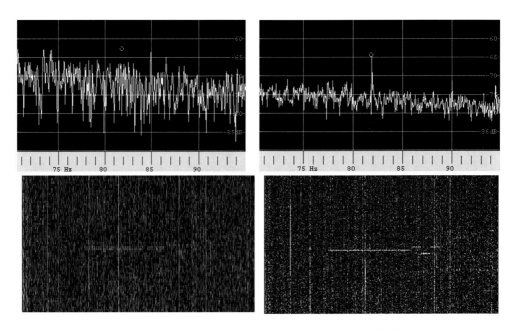

FFT gain in action on a signal reception for submarines. On the left side, spectrum and spectrogram with a 1024 point FFT, on the right side, the same signal analysed with a 16,000 point FFT: tones at 82Hz clearly emerge from hum noise (we are processing the same signal!)

185

There is no "correct setting" for an FFT, because it depends on how quickly the signal to be received evolves in time and on its reception strength with respect to noise and interference. The setting will always be a compromise.

This concept can induce confusion, because from the analysis of the recording, by just changing the FFT number points we can achieve a signal to noise ratio of 3dB or of 20dB (but we are processing the same recording, and 17dB of SNR makes a very big difference). In fact we are confronted by one of the most important principles of Fourier Analysis theory, called "FFT gain". It says that by varying the resolution (number of bars), the level of a pure signal does not vary, whilst the noise level associated to the channel does.

This is the reason why, when making the FFT of a received signal with a microphone, we can display some details which the human ear misses. The resolution of the human ear is around 10Hz, so a common FFT made with a home computer is able to reach up to signals 2000 times weaker than the most sensitive human ear can perceive. From here, it is very clear that ears able to listen to very weak signals do not exist. This is an image portrayed in many war films which show a hero telegraphist with a super ear..... the FFT analysis sent him to retirement.

FFT setting errors

It may sound like a nonsense, that whilst a "correct" setting does not exist, yet we can have real incorrect settings. We would like to accelerate the spectrogram speed while it is running on the screen, but with some programs we risk having setting errors which can jeopardize and alter the final result. While software such as Spectrogram and Spectran permit only a limited access to FFT parameters, other programs like SpectrumLab do not have any limitation, permitting us to process data in an "incorrect" way. Setting errors are possible on two parameters, the displayed frequency band and the display speed.

The frequency band we can display will depend upon the number of pixels available and on the screen resolution:

Displayed range = Available pixels x resolution

A 512 point FFT generates a 256 bar graphic display and if the space on the screen is 256 pixels, every bin generated by the FFT occupies the space of a single pixel. Practically we will have the association of one bin to one pixel, which is the optimum condition (Spectran and SpectrumLab execute this operation in an automatic and non-controllable way).

By executing a 16384 point FFT, we obtain 8192 bin (bars) which cannot be displayed in the same way on a 768 (only) vertical point screen. So we will have to select a frequency portion where the relationship of one bin to one pixel is still valid. If not, we will have a spectrogram, which does not show us all data really calculated by the program. The same thing is valid for the inverse setting; if we have 125 bin or bars, it is useless to spread them on 400 pixel because then we will have the same data represented more and more times.

Here is the same signal processed at three different resolutions:

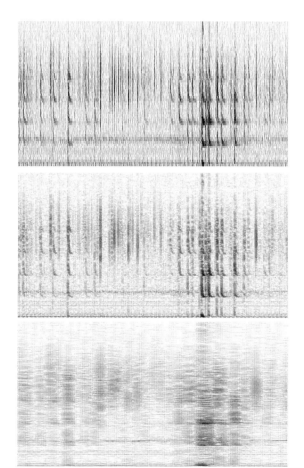

With a 64 FFT point resolution in time but at low frequencies the image seems vertically stretched

With 256 FFT point: in this case that's the best compromise between resolution in time and in frequency.

With 1024 FFT points: high resolution in frequency and less in time. The image seems horizontally stretched.

Two practical examples on another 256 pixel image:

FFT 512 pts SR = 44100, Frequency resolution = 86.1 Hz
Displayed band = 86.1 x 256 = 22050 Hz

FFT 65536 pts, SR = 44100, Frequency resolution = 0.67 Hz
Displayed band = 0.67 x 256 = 172.2 Hz

Another common setting error comes from the flow speed (the scrolling rate), indicating how often on the image of the spectrogram a vertical line must appear. The best setting is when the flow time is more or less equal to the FFT buffer filling one:

Scrolling time = 1 / Frequency Resolution
Scrolling time = Number of FFT points /Sample Rate

A faster scrolling time stretches the same data over more pixels (this is called overlap), and it extends the spectrogram in a improper way, while a too long a time does not allow us to see all bins produced by the FFT analysis on the screen. Normally, for usual analysis, an overlap up to four gives an acceptable display for almost all analyzed signals.

23. Software filtering and RDF

Software filters are not the total solution to the hum noise, because they are successive analyses of the received signal. However they do allow the reduction of an annoying hum noise to scarcely perceivable levels, without in anyway altering the characteristics of natural radio signals, such as whistlers.

Comb filters

Before the advent of modern computers, which permit the filtering of the received signal in real time, the only way to reduce the hum noise from our reception was to get far away from houses and electric lines. Nowadays FFT processing can work miracles. It does not allow us to receive natural origin radio signals inside a house, but it allows us to undertake these listening sessions in our gardens.

The ability to filter arises from the way the soundcard works. The analog input signal is sampled and transformed into numerical data. Once the signal has become a number series, we can carry out any kind of mathematical operation we want to make on it with a "calculator".

If we want to suppress for instance, 10 frequencies in a received signal, we just have to tell the computer to apply the required mathematical operation to our signal data. The same process using traditional analogue electronics (transistors, resistances, capacitors), would require a huge quantity of components, with the big disadvantage of not being easily adjustable. A low pass filter remains always a low pass filter, while, to obtain a different result, we would need to use a different type of filter. In practice we would need a separate analogue filter for every effect we want to achieve. If this is done via software, a mouse click is enough to select a filter type adapted to our situation. All these techniques require that the soundcard work in full duplex, and that is usually the case nowadays, for the majority of cards.

This programming flexibility allows us, for instance, to calculate even very complex filters, which would not be realized easily in analogue form, because they would be too complex and too expensive. A practical example is the comb filter, designed to suppress the mains frequency and its harmonics. This kind of filtering consists of a series of very narrow filters, called notches, which are tuned, for example, in the European version to 50, 150, 250, 350, ….Hz, up to 32 filters for each channel. The hum noise reduction achieved by this filter is remarkable, and it permits us to listen to signals such as whistlers, which would be otherwise hidden by the other noises.

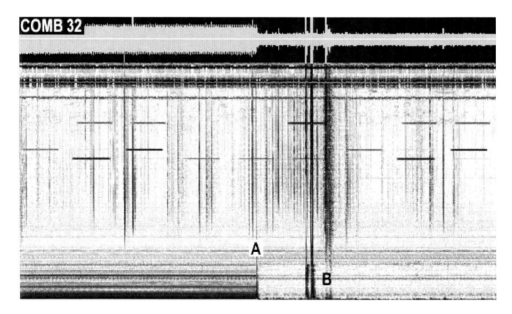

A 3 second spectrogram from 0 to 22kHz recorded close to a house. At point "A" the comb filter starts reducing the hum noise; at point "B" two statics are shown, which, under the filter effect, are "stretched" toward right.

This filter can be "built" with different options, which depend on the kind of hum noise we suffer from. If the listening is being done with a vertical electrical antenna, such as a Marconi or a whip, the best effect is obtained by filtering the 50Hz and all its odd harmonics. If we are using a loop, then because of the inductive coupling with the electric mains close to us, the best effect will be obtained by suppressing both even and odd harmonics: 50, 100, 150, 200…….Hz.

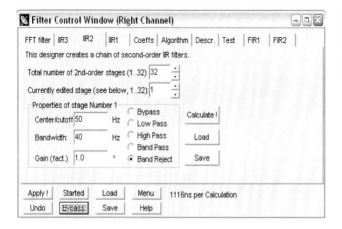

In this screen shot we can set a filter's working parameters. It is quite simple to use and it does not need us to input any computer code.

Every filter can be customised through a control panel where we can also decide the filter size and by how much the interfering signal must be suppressed (these functions are available in SpectrumLab). Useful signals are not totally "safe", though. For instance, after the comb filter action shown in the picture, the statics suffer a small "smearing", and they create a little band on the spectrogram, on the right of every single bin filter. The length of the smearing is inversely proportional to the filter bandwidth. If it is 1Hz wide it will produce a 1 second smear, while a 10Hz large filter will only produce a 0.1 sec smear. A good compromise for this kind of filter is for a 20Hz bandwidth.

Filters based on delay and HUMID

Another way to eliminate hum noise relies on delay techniques. Even this process can be achieved in real time by the soundcard with software like Spectran or SpectrumLab.

The technique, which is simple but very clever, was first proposed by Eric Vogel who is Swedish, and was then improved by American Paul Nicholson, who called it HUMID: Hum Instant Destroyer. The filtering is achieved by utilizing a part of the signal to eliminate the hum. The input signal is split in two equal parts, and one of them is delayed by "1 / mains frequency" (20ms to suppress the 50Hz and 16.66 ms to suppress the 60Hz), then its polarity is inverted (positive parts are exchanged with negative ones) and it is summed to the other part.

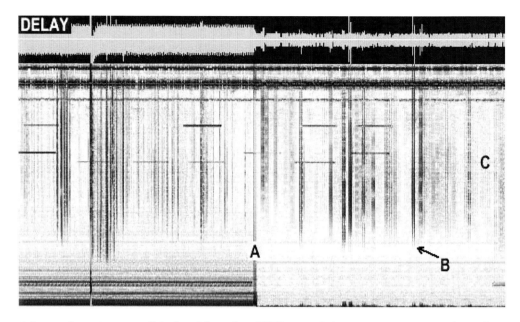

A 3 second spectrogram of the band from 0 to 22kHz recorded close to a house. At point "A" we can see the filter in action, at point "B" a discharge splitting effect, and in C point some Alpha signals disappear because they are at multiple of the mains frequency

The result is excellent, when the mains frequency and its harmonics are added to their exact opposite and they give absolute silence, so that at 50, 100, 150 ... Hz (or 60,120, 180 ... Hz) there is no signal. The effect is similar to a comb filter but it has no limits in frequency because it works over the whole soundcard frequency band. The "collateral damage" is caused by the signal splitting which produces a kind of echo visible on the spectrogram close to a static. We can hear an echo return as if we were in a long empty corridor. This effect is also called discharge tube. A small echo is much more acceptable than the hum noise.

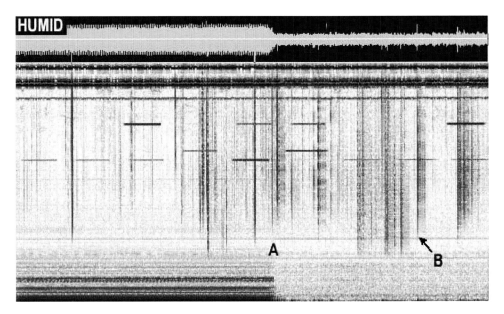

Same conditions with HUMID filter: Alpha signals are now all present but the echo effect on the statics (B) becomes more visible

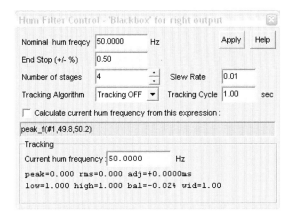

HUMID filter console, using SpectrumLab software.

A big choice of parameters is available to reduce the filter effect according to environmental listening conditions

Through the process called Humid, the technique is applied more than once to the same signal, decreasing the echo back effect, which is present with the simple single delay method.

The FFT filter

A more recent filtering technique, presented by Wolfgang Busher in his SpectrumLab, uses the FFT analysis results as a noise reduction system. The program separates the signal in many small frequency segments, analyzing them one by one, and where a signal is found to be continuous it is erased.

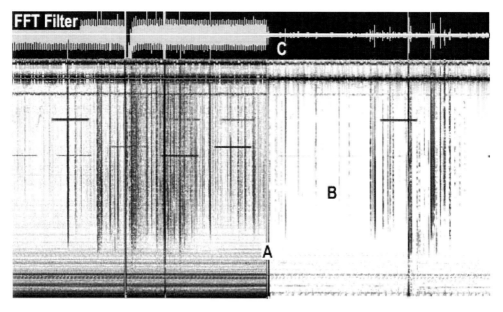

A 3 seconds spectrogram of the band from 0 to 22kHz recorded near a house. The FFT filter reduces the noise until it totally disappears (A and C points).The weakest signals such as far away statics or weak whistlers, also disappear, which leaves only the hiss noise.

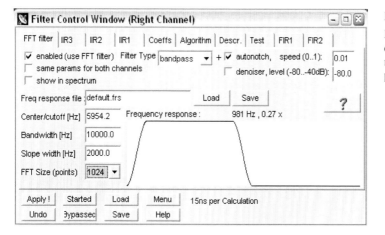

FFT filter console.
Its use is not difficult, but it does need a little of practice.

The effect on noise is dramatic, because all those signals having a continuous character (such as hum noise) are recognized and suppressed, while the shorter signals, such as statics, tweeks and whistlers are not disturbed and pass through the filter.

The "collateral effect" of this filter is an unnatural timbre of the audible signal, which is somewhat similar to the listening of a conversation on a mobile GSM phone with low signal. Even in this case, these small distortions caused by the filter, are acceptable because the hum noise disappears.

Complex FFT (RDF or radio-localization)

When you go on a medium size boat you will often see, near to the radar antennas, a strange fixed structure, consisting of two circular loops, set at 90° to each other. These are radio-location antennas where by processing the signals received simultaneously by the two loops we can derive the direction of an incoming signal, without needing to rotating the loops.

The signal induces voltages on the two loops at very slightly different times, and by analysing this difference in phase between the outputs of two loops, it is possible, by receiving say a long-wave lighthouse radio transmission, to calculate the direction of the lighthouse and thus the position of the ship.

This process can work the same way at VLF, and by connecting two receiving loops (for instance a couple of EasyLoops from chapter 7), in an orthogonal position to the two soundcard inputs, we can obtain information giving the direction of arrival of a signal.

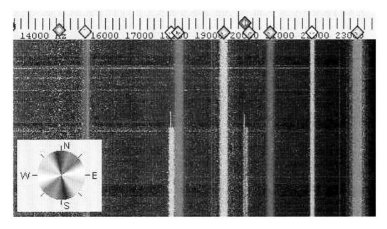

In this picture is a spectrogram where (on screen) colors give the direction of the signals

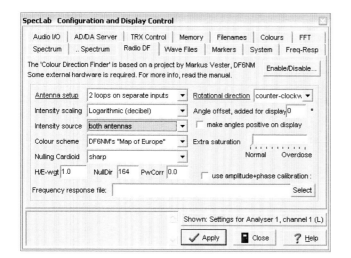

Settings for obtaining the RDF function in the SpectrumLab program

The complex calculation is done within SpectrumLab and the spectrogram produced displays for each signal, its intensity, and direction. Every colour corresponds to a direction and the colour saturation corresponds to the signal intensity level. We can also obtain similar results with earth dipoles.

These techniques can have very interesting applications in the seismic precursor field, because knowing where a signal comes from can help to associate it with a seismic event or not. Thus allowing us to exclude other signals, which have nothing to do with this event, because they originate in areas remote from the earthquake.

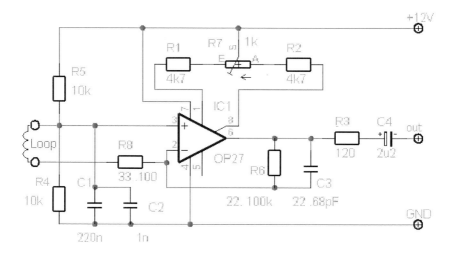

A circuit of an amplifier used with two orthogonal loops on a ferrite core employed as an RDF antenna. Circuit by Wolfgang Buscher DL4YHF

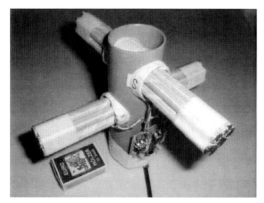

An orthogonal loop built by using ferrite coming from old AM radios antennas.

Using two active loops, directly connected to the soundcard, permits us to determinate the signal direction but with an ambiguity. That is we know the angle, but do not know if the signal comes from behind or in front. To determinate the direction unambiguously we must add in the signal from a third vertical antenna, often called the "sense antenna". This project requires an additional analogue channel, which is rather complex, and therefore it will not be explained in this book.

24. Network observatory

The major difference between a researcher from the 1980s and his present day colleague is undoubtedly the huge quantity of data available to him on the net today, to compare with his own reception and findings. Recordings can be compared to seismic data, geomagnetic index, solar activity and all the other physical data nowadays monitored. Here we will review websites giving useful observations for a cross comparison with VLF reception.

From website WetterZentrale we can have access to a map of storm activity all over Europe, with the time and place where lightning is discharging. This is very helpful information for studying statics, tweeks and an indispensable support for seismic precursor research, to avoid confusing normal storm activity with eventual rock emissions under tektonic stress. The website presents the situation over the last 24 hours and the complete filing of the data collected by its own observation station.

http://www.wetterzentrale.de

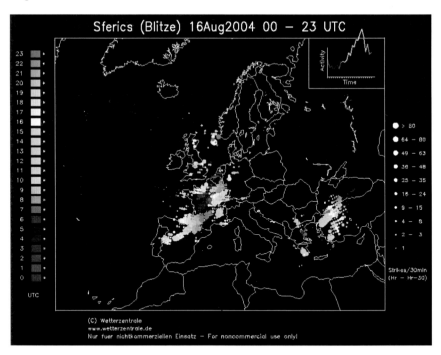

An example of a storm activity map for Europe. We can follow the time, place and intensity of the phenomena. Similar maps are available on the Internet for the whole planet, updated in real time.

We can obtain data about Schumann Resonances from the well known University of California, Berkeley, where their intensity is constantly monitored together with the resonance of a single frequency. Because of the dimension of the wave length of the resonances (7.8Hz corresponds to 38500km wave length), we can assume the data is also valid at our latitudes, assuming global spread is quite uniform.

ftp://quake.geo.berkeley.edu/pub/em/

The homepage where the different activities are explained is:
http://quake.geo.berkeley.edu/

The Space Environment Center provides real time monitoring and forecasting of Solar and Geophysical events, it also researches conditions on the Sun and Earth and develops techniques for forecasting Solar and Geophysical disturbances. SEC is jointly operated by NOAA and by American Military Aviation and it is the world's most important centre for electro-magnetic disturbance monitoring, used by all who work in the space field. The homepage is:

http://www.sec.noaa.gov/

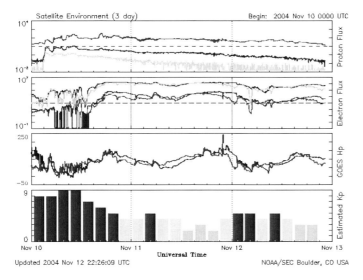

The table covers three days' solar activity

Amongst the data available from SEC about VLF activity, for instance, is the last three days situation for Solar wind, X-ray flux and Geo-magnetic activity, whilst forecasting for the next three days is also available on this page:

http://www.sec.noaa.gov/today.html

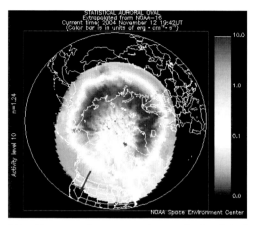

At the same time it is possible to view auroral activity produced by solar wind, with a real time map,

http://www.sel.noaa.gov/pmap/index.html

Another very good website with solar activity data is "Lockheed Martin Solar and Astrophysics Laboratory", which is at the Lockheed Martin Advanced Technology Center (ATC) in Palo Alto, California. This is a science and engineering group project to design and construct instrumentation for astrophysical and solar monitoring. Here again Solar radiation flux, Solar wind and Geo-magnetic activity data are available. The homepage is: http://www.lmsal.com

While the big page about solar activity data is:

http://www.lmsal.com/solarsoft/latest_events/

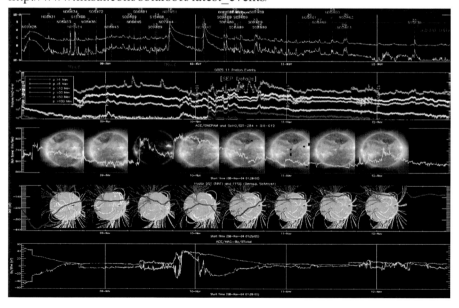

Also in Europe some research organisations exist which share data on the Internet. The Swedish Space Physics Institute is a government body with 110 employees, and its activities are based around space technology, physics and atmospheric structure. Homepage:

http://spider.irf.se

The headquarters is in Kiruna, from where is possible to access magnetograms, riometer graphs and ionoprobe graphs. Data can be consulted on:

http://spider.irf.se/mag/

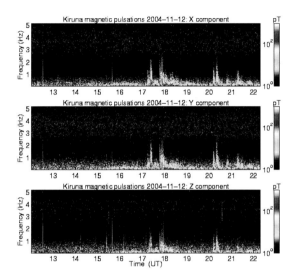

Spectrogram from Kiurna Observatory magneto-meters, concerning magnetic activity at below 5Hz.

The three spectrograms show the data coming from three sensors North-South, East–West oriented and vertical .

Another important solar and electro-magnetic data resource is at HAARP (High Frequency Active Auroral Research Program). We have already mentioned their activities, where many kinds of instruments, operate twenty-four hours a day, without interruption, magneto-meters, riometers, ionoprobes, cameras etc. Their homepage is:

http://www.haarp.alaska.edu/haarp/index.html

The page where is possible to download or display instrument data is:

http://www.haarp.alaska.edu/haarp/data.fcgi

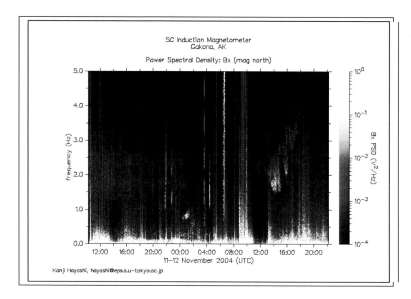

SC Induction Magnetometer
Gakona, AK

Power Spectral Density: Bx (mag north)

Kanji Hayashi, hayashi@eps.s.u-tokyo.ac.jp

A magnetic pulsation –type 1- recorded in Alaska by the HAARP magnetometer.

A very useful tool also are the mailing lists, you can register to receive a message every time the solar index shows instability. The most popular site is Space Weather.

http://spaceweather.com

This has news and information about solar activity and about the main astronomic events, for example near-Earth passes by asteroids. Their web page for subscriptions is:

http://science.nasa.gov/news/subscribe.asp?checked=sw

Last but not least, we cite websites which collect seismic activity data. If we look for radio precursors and if we have a quite large amount of ELF and ULF radio activity data, it is important to make a comparison with all seismic activity, however small, occurring during our recording period.

There are small local networks all over the planet, which can provide accurate data about their particular area. We will just mention, as an example, two of them, in Northern Italy.

Volcanology and Geo-physics Institute, called MedNet (Mediterranean very broadband seismo-graphic network) has its homepage on:

http://mednet.ingv.it/

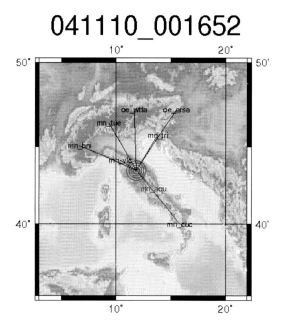

041110_001652

The image on the left maps a seismic event showing the epicenter, and tracing of the different seismic observing points, with date and time of the earthquake.

Similar information, with even more detail, about Northern Italy monitoring can be obtained from DIP.TE.RIS (Genoa University Territory and Resources Study Department) the net is called RSNI (Regional Seismic Network of Norwest Italy). Its web address is: http://www.dipteris.unige.it/geofisica/

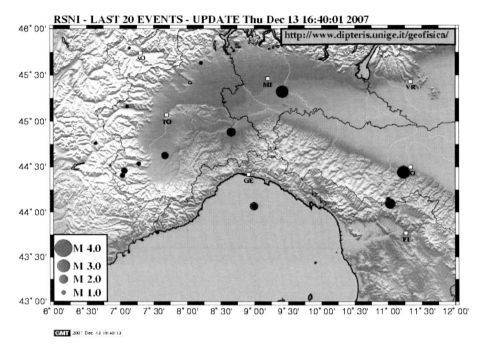

In the map of Northern Italy above is the location and intensity of the last 20 seismic events. This service provides maps of the events and distributes a complete list of observations as is shown here.

```
Manual Picking - Update: Fri Nov 12 16:40:00 2004
ORIGIN TIME (UTC) LATITUDE LONGITUDE DEPTH  Md NF GAP D3  RMS ERH ERZ Q
041031 2133 52.06 44N26.55 7E17.16 10.03  16 8 218 22.1 .04 2.6 3.4 C
041101 1158 42.30 44N31.39 6E44.40 10.55  23 26 231 54.1 .06  .5  .5 C
041101 1326 4.30 44N18.91 7E35.56 10.93  25 31 65 22.6 .10  .4  .8 B
041101 2116 42.20 44N 8.10 8E 0.85  2.09  19 12 151 21.6 .17 2.7 6.1 C
041102 126 54.53 44N53.80 6E45.83  8.80  19 11 238 40.0 .11 1.4 1.3 C
... .
```

Worldwide seismic data are provided by USGS, the United States Geological Survey. The institute works with some other bodies such as NEHRP (earthquake risk reduction program) and NIST (National Institute Standard and Technology). Website is:

http://earthquake.usgs.gov/

Most recent earthquakes are available on:
http://earthquake.usgs.gov/recenteqsww/

Observations over the entire European zone are available on:
http://earthquake.usgs.gov/recenteqsww/Maps/region/Europe.html

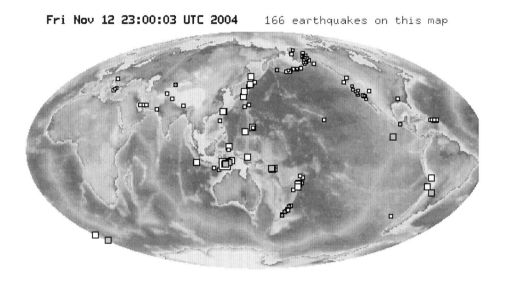

Worldwide earthquake map.

25. Pseudoscience: what natural origin radio signals are not

For practical and technical reasons, some select frequencies which they believe possess a special significance. Like all mysterious knowledge it takes just few numerical coincidences with cerebral frequencies or with "cosmic vibrations" (as metaphysical sciences such as Feng-Shui suggest) to transform VLF into a "mystery kingdom".

Roaming the Internet world it is possible to find a whole range of "information" relating to VLF, and thought conditioning, communication with your own spirit guide, alien transmissions, geo-pathogenic (Hartmann Knots), climatic event control, and much more. It is amazing to see how sometimes reality could be surpassed by a wild hypothesis which has no practical, theoretical, or mathematical support.

We do not want to discuss every single detail here but, we would just like to list the major hypotheses of these disciplines and the reason why the laws of physics cause them to be referred to as "pseudo-sciences".

Electroencephalograms and thought transmission

Our brain works by exchanging information between its different parts through electrical impulses. These impulses operate mainly at very low frequencies, which would be in the ULF band. To every cerebral activity there is corresponding emission at various frequencies, as the following table shows.

Brain Waves	Frequency Range	Brain Activity
Delta	From 0.5 to 4Hz	Deep Sleep
Theta	From 4 to 8Hz	Sleepiness
Alpha	From 8 to 14Hz	Conscious relaxing
Beta	From 14 to 30Hz	Concentration

An association between ULF waves and thought transmission has been suggested by many people, and we have a huge quantity of fascinating hypotheses around the subject. Analyzing this topic from a mathematical and scientific stand-point, changes and reshapes the idea: let's see how and why.

Our brain does not have a standard electrical (circuit) structure, but every single person has his own personal cerebral electrical brain structure, formed by making billions of inter-connections, and belonging only to him as a biologically unique being. This means that a micro-current flowing in XY brain coordinates, if applied in another person will take a different meaning. Even supposing to be able to use a machine to simultaneously reproduce the thousands of tiny electric currents which flow in a human being's brain, they would be valid for that person only, or at least for a brain, completely identical cell by cell.

To use a metaphor, we can compare our brain to a metropolis with its city plan. If we go in another city with the same map we will soon become lost, because neither streets, nor avenues, nor squares would correspond.

Hypothesizing that two brains could communicate between them through ULF is like saying that to exchange data between two computers all we have to do is just connect them with an electric cable, at *any point* on the two machines. It just would not work of course, or worse, the two computers could even be damaged. Those who work with computers know how difficult it is to make two computers communicate with each other, despite all machines having a hardware interface and software created for the purpose of this kind of data exchange. Our brain doesn't have this hardware, or software.

This subject is not sustainable even physically, because the ULF currents circulating in our brain are measured in nano-amperes (one billionth part of an ampere) and they run for only some millimeters in distance. The energy emitted by these impulses is around one nW (a billionth part of watt). There is no real signal radiation, as it happens in an antenna, and to keep tabs on cerebral activity, the electrodes of the EEG are placed directly on the skin, in order to pick up some of the currents. An antenna placed near the patient to receive the RF field would not give any result.

The only thing that in some way is radiated beyond our skull is the magnetic field induced by these currents. For few centimeters over our hair it is possible to receive this magnetic field with very sensitive sensors called SQUID, which become hyper-conductors after they have been put in liquid helium at very low temperatures. Through a 150 sensor electro-encephalogram we can gain a very good appreciation of the currents flowing, whilst with the new magneto-encephalogram non-invasive techniques (using SQUID), we are able to to follow activity in our brain to with a ¼ mm resolution.

In practical terms this means that the very weak ULF band signal induced by our brain is not radiating and so it cannot be used by another similar biological device, and more than this, it weakens quickly just few centimeters over our head. After that it becomes completely submerged beyond detection by the natural environmental hum noise, such as the Schumann Resources and the radio-electric noises, which are always present around us.

It is true that submarines use signals right in these bands and that these signals propagate with very low attenuations throughout the whole planet, penetrating even the deepest ocean salt water layers. It is also true that to be radiated, these radio waves need to be produced with millions of watts of radio-electric power, and antennas many kilometers long as are used by military communications.

Despite all this, we do not want to exclude the possibility that telepathy exists, but we just wish to state that ULF waves are simply not sufficient to sustain this phenomenon.

Shumann resonances and health

It is very well known by those who work with electroencephalograms that frequencies of our cerebral activity are similar to those of the Schumann Resonances, and, at the same time, we know that the impedance value read between needles in pinprick therapy (acupuncture) has a similar frequency.

It would be only too simple to search for what effect the frequency and intensity variations of Schumann Resonances could have on our brain functioning. Many studies have been done for this purpose, but results, so far, are not very encouraging. Very serious scientific researches demonstrate a connection between some chemical compounds in our bodies, such as Melatonin, and the presence or not of a magnetic signal at the first Schumann Resonance (7.8Hz). We can say the same thing for the electro-magnetic fields at low frequency. The strange thing is that by increasing the signal intensity, the phenomenon disappears. It is like saying that after drinking a glass of wine we are not longer thirsty, with four glasses we are drunk and with two hundred nothing happens.

If Schumann Resonances did have an influence on our cerebral and biological activities we should also associate them to the electro-magnetic pollution levels at low frequency in our homes, which are millions of times more intense than are the Schumann Resonances. If our body perceives so weak a signal as natural resonances including Schumann Resonances, would not it be devastated by the strong signals coming from electric mains? For the moment we do not have any answer to this question.

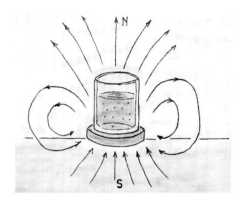

Another recent kind of business: magnetic water.

The magnetizer device in the lower part of the glass (a simple magnet) would permit the water to become "magnetized". This water, once consumed, could give to our body all the "needed" magnetism

Many firms have already started to produce and commercialise "health generators", which are devices able to generate a magnetic field at the first Schumann Resonance. According to producers, the object would stimulate cerebral activity at work so increasing the worker's performance, and of course one device is needed for each room.

Meantime if the owner of a company wishes to improve the productivity of his employees with some thousands of €uros, he can make magnetic oscillations in the working area at 7.8Hz (... shouldn't we reduce the electro-magnetic pollution?). Recent experiments done by Italian universities were not able to show and prove a connection between cerebral activity and Schumann Resonances. Some experiments done in a cave, where people had no reference to night and day periodicity, seem more optimistic, but these conditions are very far from reality and can have only an experimental character.

This subject matter is also closely related to low frequency electro-magnetic pollution effects, in other words, it is connected to any effects on our health from 50Hz mains, and this is presently the object of scientific research. Hopefully what the researchers are now studying and experiencing will give us in a future some very important answers.

Hartmann's knots

Professor Ernst Hartmann was an independent German researcher, who became very famous in the 1950s for his theories about geo-pathologies, in other words, the connection between the occurrence of illness and the place and mode of residence. We are not able to talk about real theories, since Hartmann never gave any physical evidence, or mathematical proof of what he claimed. It would thus be more exact to call them hypotheses, and below are some of his ideas.

Hartmann argued that the earth was the centre of magnetic field and that there were invisible energies, coming from its centre and radiating out towards the whole universe, then joining the "cosmic energy". During this radiating effect, forces are deviated by internal movements of the Earth, and by minerals, and crystals underground. This distortion takes the form of an invisible grid on the earth surface, consisting of bands in North-South and East-West directions 20 centimeters wide and a couple of meters apart, transforming the Earth's surface into a big paper sheet with two meter squares on it.

These bands are a kind of shade zone and inside it the "terrestrial energy" is weakened. Where these bands intersect East-West and North–South, the shading effect is multiplied and it can become dangerous to our health. These crossing zones are called Cancer Zones, or cosmic perturbations or Hartmann's Knots.

Magnetic meridians and parallels cross each other forming a Hartmann knot.

Would you sleep in your bed without cleaning your room if someone told you the room is a cancer knot?

A medium size apartment (according this theory) could therefore host one or two dozen Hartmann Knots. These Knots move according to what happens underground (as for instance the lowering of the phreatic water table), and also according to the terrestrial electro-magnetic pollution.

Remaining long, or sleeping over a Hartmann Knot could provoke, according to Hartmann, chronic illness such as cancer, psychological syndromes, divorces and sudden death.

We can imagine how can be successful (or at least lucrative) the "environment reclamation" operators work was. "Environment reclamation", or "drainage", is achieved by localizing the position of the knots in the apartment, and then, if possible, moving beds and furniture out of these areas. When this is not possible, the work is done using copper coins or cork discs, so that the non-covered areas are enlarged.

Rabdomancy has popular and very old origins. The dowser was considered able to localize the presence of water, metal and other negative energies coming from the underground.

Picture comes from *Scienza e Paranormale*, a CICAP magazine .

The knot detection is achieved by a water-diviner (dowser) action, the dowser using his sensitivity to magnetic fields, defines the presence and the disposition of the entire net. Sometimes some electronic devices are used as a support such as saturation magnetometers or electric field meters, or else a transmitter may be placed in a corner of the room with a receiver whose signal is affected by the propagation knots. It is stressed that this instrumentation is only a support, because the main agent for localizing the knots still is the water diviner.

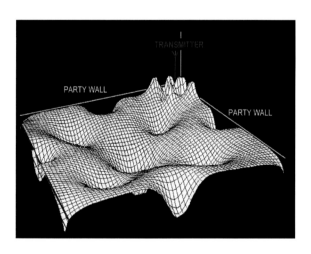

Hartmann Knots can be observed by a transmitter placed in a corner of a room and by a receiver observing the emitted field.

This kind of representation is very well known in the mobile phone field and it is called the Rayleigh Universe; it is as if we light a room with a light bulb placed under the table we observe the shadows

The doubts we have about actual scientific knowledge in this subject are pretty clear:

1) According to Hartmann's theory, rays radiated by the Earth to form the network would travel in a straight line. Since this energy is deemed to be magnetic energy, there is no physical law which exists explaining the presence of magnetic

211

field flux lines which do not close in a loop such as happens with a magnet. There are no mathematical rules describing these flux lines and they have never been measured. Maxwell's equations about magnetism, dating to more than 100 years ago, are still the basis for today's telecommunication systems, and are regularly validated experimentally. Millions of mobile phones in our countries are seen to support Maxwell's theory, and not Hartmann's, who, despite many requests, never gave any explanation of these phenomena (someone has said he even confused electric field flux lines and magnetic field lines).

2) According to Hartmann, rays would be influenced by different factors, such as water and ELF fields. Although actual knowledge states that a variable magnetic field at 50Hz cannot influence the level of a continuous magnetic field, and neither can water courses, or copper or cork discs, which, as we know, are all non-magnetic materials.

3) According to Hartmann, rays would not be measurable, but, with the help of today's technologies, it is hard to think of any terrestrial natural phenomena which cannot be measured, particularly if they have a well defined physical size. The explanation proposed by Hartmann was extremely clear. He said they are not measurable because only a "medium" could feel them, with his magnetic receptors.

4) Modern medical magnetic resonance techniques have explained another crucial point: Hartmann's magnetic receptors are not present in human beings, while they are present in some birds which use them to for orientation during migration flights.

Everyone of us can of course believe in what he or she likes, but it is not true that we don't have any scientific evidence about this subject. All tests, so far, show in a very clear and unequivocal way the absence of this phenomenon. Technically, we can only say that neither saturation magnetometers (described in precedent chapters), nor static field meters, can observe any of the anomalies in electrical or magnetic field distribution, postulated by Dr. Hartmann.

Alien signals and voices from the "afterlife"

This mystery is possibly of more concern to people who take care of the human psyche than researchers studying radio signals. The connections between VLF and dead people or between VLF and alien civilizations have never been explained by those who claim to be followers of these kind of theories and hypotheses. Despite years and years of research in this field there are no recordings able to bring us to think of something "strange" despite the very high sensitivity of the devices employed and despite the seriousness with which the experiments were done.

We mention this subject in this book because through the Internet site www.vlf.it there are many people, sending E-Mail from all over the world, who ask the site author for information about these "borderline subjects" or, worse still, they propose collaborations linking VLF and prophecies, VLF and religion, VLF and demons... and other debates which have nothing to do with scientific research. Two brief commentaries about this topic follow.

Supposing there is a possible contact with a civilization external to the Earth, it is really improbable that this contact would happen in the VLF frequency range. Very long waves are very difficult to transmit because of the antenna dimension, and they can transport very little information at a time due the limited bandwidth. Also, they are in the middle of the most powerful radio emission phenomena caused by natural events. So, the audio band is usually busy, and it would be like whispering in a place where everyone else is screaming very loud. If we are to look for ET, there are certainly better chances of success pointing by UHF TV antenna toward the sky than monitoring the electric field at audio frequencies. This is another story and it belongs to SETI.

Concerning the "voices": it will happen to every one of us, sooner or later, to be in the sad situation of mourning a loved one. The desire for contact, which is no longer possible, can push us to read some data in an irrational way, especially if in this situation there are people who seek to take advantage of us.

Technically we have to remember that voices could come out from a VLF receiver, mainly at night time. These are caused by receiver overload, caused by strong short wave signals (as we described in chapter six, in that part concerning inter-modulation). These voices are subjected to the typical fading of short wave propagation, and for this reason a voice can suddenly appear saying some words before disappearing again. Some ionospheric cross modulation produces very "ethereal" sounds due to the filtering effect of the generation process.

The effect is technically similar to the one reproduced when we listen to our home telephone whilst our neighbour is trying his CB transmitter. This effect could easily happen with the very simple receivers that are used on VLF, when they are connected to very big antennas. The phenomenon is very sporadic, so it is not worth complicating our listening sessions with a more complex receiver, and we just have to be able to recognize the effect for what it is.

Conclusions

Since you have now arrived at the end of this book, you should have a quite precise idea about the signals and the possibilities offered in this field of research. This treatise was written with a double purpose: it can be an introduction for those who had already heard about VLF, and wished to learn more about it; it can also be a starting point from where to move to study in more depth, the aspects that we particularly enjoy.

Every subject described in every single chapter, can be studied more deeply and could become subject of another book. There is quite a lot of material available on the Internet and using any search engine we can search for VLF and whistlers and we will be soon submerged by tons of documents, including some very high level theses.

Since I began my interest and study of VLF listening, I have never had available a basic text explaining VLF generation and propagation concepts to me. I also missed the practical applications and the access to the technical knowledge base that are often beyond the resources of a home researcher. This is what I've tried to provide for you in this book: I hope I have succeeded.

This book is the literal transposition of my experience with web site: www.vlf.it, a virtual research laboratory for VLF, born on June 1999 and which has become a worldwide exchange portal for those who enjoy and study VLF and natural radio signals. The site stays active due to the work of many spontaneous collaborators who share their VLF experiences by writing articles about their experiments. The majority of these are carried out with home made equipment, or they are done with very cheap and easily available materials. A quick look at the projects can give you more precise instructions about how to design receivers and reception techniques. On such an unusual subject, just reading a book can sometimes be not enough.

Suggestions for further reading:

If you wish to deepen your knowledge of whistlers you can find one the most complete treaties in: *Whistlers and Related Ionospheric Phenomena* by Robert A. Helliwell, and published for the first time by Stanford University, California in 1965(!). VLF was studied mainly for military purposes, given the political situation at that time, in order to see how it could be used. The book is very technically accurate despite the very little, and relatively poor, technology available 40 years ago. The text is in English and quite high level. This has recently been reissued by Dover and is available via Amazon and other retailers.

Another standard text about whistlers and VLF by two Japanese researchers, and always a good reference point, is: *Natural VLF Radio Waves* by Toshimi Okada and Akira Iwai, published by Research Studies Press Ltd, England. This book (1988) is one of the most complete treatises about this matter. The text is in English but is quite difficult reading.

The LWCA, Long Wave Club of America, has on its site: www.lwca.org a huge collection of data about the subject. Periodic editions of "The Lowdown", always have a section devoted to Radio Nature.

The American website www.auroralchorus.com, by Steve McGreevy, offers a signal collection recorded in wave format. These are very nice signals and in some cases very rare. There is also a guide about how to build a VLF receiver.

RTTY and utility addresses are also available on the web site www.vlf.it with a very complete list in sections: ELF and VLF frequency Guide, by Trond Jacobsen and Long Wave RDF Project by Manfred Kerckhoff.

If you want more detail on the geomagnetic pulsation subject, you can find a very interesting website of the University of Oulu, Finland at http://www.oulu.fi/~spaceweb/textbook/content.html: The text of "Space physics textbook" is in english, with many pictures and it is a very complete coverage of the subject, containing topics as Sun, Magnetosphere, Ionosphere, Geomagnetic activity, Aurora and some others.

A good guide to understanding how the PC soundcard works, how it is used for receiving and displaying VLF signals, and how to install an automatic monitoring statiom, is "Spectrum laboratory index", by Wolfgang Buescher. This is the guide to the SpectrumLab program suite. The text (more than 150 pages) is available from website: http://freenet-homepage.de/dl4yhf/ and is in English.

For a scientific approach to borderline sciences, or pseudosciences, such as telepathy, geo-pathogeny and many others, a good support can be Piero Angela's book: *Viaggio nel mondo paranormale* (Travel in the paranormal world), first published by Mondadori in 2000.

If you want to be very pragmatic, on the same subject you can link to www.cicap.org: (Comitato Italiano per il Controllo delle Affermazioni sul Paranormale), where you can find many articles about experiments very seriously carried out. Italian version only, but very easy to read. Cicap is connected with other international organizations as CSICOP (Committee for the Scientific Investigation of Claims of the Paranormal, http://www.csicop.org/) and The Skeptical Society (http://www.skeptic.com/).

Details about signals for submarine communication: *Reception of ELF signals at antipodal distances*. Antony C. Fraser-Smith, STAR Laboratory, Stanford University, Stanford, CA 94305; Peter R. Bannister, 154 Nebraska Circle, Sebastian, Florida 32958.

A very good article about antennas used to receive signals whilst submerged is: 'Towed antennas for US submarine communications: a historical perspective', . by David F. Rivera and Rajeev Bansal, from: *IEEE Antennas and Propagation Magazine, Vol.46, n.1*, Feb. 2004

References:

These are for the main part available on the Internet, in PDF format. Some of them are essential, some others very accurate and specific; in some documents certain topics are claimed which are denied in the other ones. If a matter is particularly interesting to you, we suggest you study the topic consulting all the references about it.

Schumann Resonances, a plausible biophysical mechanism for the human health effects of Solar/Geomagnetic Activity, Neil Cherry, Environmental Management and Design Division, Lincoln University, Canterbury, New Zealand, 9/8/2001

Investigations of Relatively Easy To Construct Antennas With Efficiency in Receiving Schumann Resonances, Preparations for a Miniaturized Reconfigurable ELF Receiver, Brian W. Farmer and Robert C. Hannan, Langley Research Center, Hampton, Virginia, NASA/TM-2003-212647 October 2003

Journal of Atmospheric and Solar-Terrestrial Physics 65 (2003) 607–614, 'Validation of sprite-inducing cloud-to-ground lightning based on ELF observations at Syowa station in Antarctica', Mitsuteru Satoa;*, Hiroshi Fukunishia, Masayuki Kikuchib, Hisao Yamagishib.

FGM-series Magnetic Field Sensors, Speake & Co Limited application note

High resolution data logger, Low cost data loggers and PC-Based Test and Measurement, Pico Technology, ADC Series application notes

Evidence for Electromagnetic Emission During Rock Loading and Fracture: A Way Towards an Earthquake Precursor, M. Caputo Dipartimento di Fisica, Università di Roma "La Sapienza", Rome Italy, 22° Convegno Nazionale Gruppo Nazionale Geofisica Terra Solida , 163-165, 18-20 November 2003.

Space Based Instrumentation for Future Detection of Artificial ULF/ELF/VLF waves and Their Effects using the Canadian Sponsored, Enhanced Polar Outflow Project (ePOP) Satellite, Paul Bernhardt, Carl Siefring, Andrew Yau, H. Gordon James, Naval Research Laboratory, Washington, DC; University of Calgary, Alberta, Canada; Communication Research Centre, Ottawa, Ontario, Canada

ELF/VLF Wave-Injection via Modulated HF Heating of the Ionosphere, Umran S. Inan, Space, Telecommunications and Radioscience Laboratory, Stanford University, Stanford, California 94305

Observation of co.seismic electromagnetic phenomena in VHF associated with Geiyo earthquake in 2001, Teruaki Yoshida and Masahiro Nishi, Faculty of Information Sciences, Hiroshima City University

Earthquake effects in the ionosphere according to Intercosmos-19 and AUREOL-3 satellite data, O.A. Molchanov with Larkina V.I. et al., Cepadues Edition, Toulouse, 685-695, 1984.)

'Typical features of excitation of low frequency emission in the upper ionosphere above earthquake areas', O.A. Molchanov with Larkina V.I. et al., *Geomagnetism and Aeronomy*, 28, 802-806, 1988.

Costruzione di uno strumento EFM, Valter Gennaro sett 2003, La Biblioteca dei 500 (rivista di scienza online di Ulisse, il portale di informazione scientifica della SISSA. http://ulisse.sissa.it)

Onde Radio Nella Banda LF e Precursori Sismici, Rodolfo Manno, Michele Caputo, Dip. di Fisica, Università degli Studi "La sapienza" Comitato Italiano per il Progetto Hessdalen

'Variations in Schumann resonances and their relation to atmospheric electric parameters at Nagycenk station', F. MaÈrcz, G. SaÂtori, B. Zieger, Geodetic and Geophysical Research Institute of the Hungarian Academy of Sciences, H 9401 Sopron, POB 5, Hungary, Received: 22 May 1996 / Revised: 4 June 1997 / Accepted: 6 June 1997, Ann. *Geophysicae 15, 1604±1614* (1997) " EGS ± Springer-Verlag 1997

I nodi di Hartmann e le geopatologie, di Roberto Vanzetto, 17.03.2004 http://www.torinoscienza.it 2002 Provincia di Torino

Phys. Chem. EarthVol. 26 2001, 'Disturbances in LF Radio Signals and the Umbria-Marche (Italy) Seismic sequence in 1997-1998', P.F. Biagi, A. Ermini, S.P. Kingsley, Dip. Fisica Università di Bari, Dip. Fisica Università di Roma, Università di Sheffield

Natural Hazards and EarthSystem Sciences 04, 2001, 'Possible eartquake precursors reveales by LF radio signals', P.F.Biagi, R.Piccolo, A. Ermini, S. Martellucci, C. Bellucci, M. Hayakawa, V. Capozzi and S.P. Kingsley, Dip Fisica Università di Bari, Dip. Fisica Università di Roma, INFM Università di Roma, Dip. Ing. Elettronica, Univ. Tokyo, Fac. Medicina e Ist. Naz. Condenser Matter, Università di Foggia, Sheffield Centre for EarthObservation science, University of Sheffield.

Atti Ticinensi della Terra, vol.43 (2002), 'Sulla possibile origine, propagazione e rivelabilità dei precursori elettromagnetici dei terremoti', E.R. Mognaschi, Dip. Fisica A. Volta, Università di Pavia, Istituto Nazionale Fisica della Materia, Unità di Pavia

Radioonde, n. 18 marzo 2000, 'Precursori elettromagnetici dei sismi, il primo anno di sperimentazione in Lunigiana', E.R. Mognaschi

Radioonde, n. 12 maggio 98, 'Precursori elettromagnetici dei sismi', E.R. Mognaschi

Radioonde, n. 22 maggio 2001, 'Evidenze di emissioni elettromagnetiche in rocce sottoposte a sollecitazione meccanica. Un possibile precursore sismico?', Adriano Nardi

Radioonde, n. 31 novemre 2003, 'First International Workshop on earthquake prediction, Earthquake source localization by means of electromagnetic precursors'. E.R. Mognaschi e M.E. Mognaschi

Radioonde, N. 32 febbraio 2004, 'La stazione di Pavia per la ricezione dei precursori elettromagnetici dei sismi', E.R. Mognaschi

Acknowledgements

A special thanks to Andrea Bertocchi who took care of the English version, and Alan Melia who read and amended the English version to put it into everyday English.

To Marco Bruno for his technical support and for the instrumentation provided by Spin Electronics.

To Ezio Mognaschi (recently passed away) of Physics University of Pavia for the scientific revision, and for the support and provided material.

To Jader Monari of the Radio Astronomic Medicine Observatory (CNR) for technical revision.

To Wolfgang Buscher for adapting time after time the SpectrumLab software to this activity's demands.

To Enrica Solaro and Michel André for the graphic support.

Also I'd like to thank all the people who, through the site www.vlf.it, have collaborated by sending articles and documentation, giving so big a contribution to this site's popularity, and giving me the strength to write this book: Andrea Borgnino, Alberto Di Bene, Vittorio De Tomasi, Giuseppe Accardo, Alan Scremin, Gianni Boscolo, Claudio Parmigiani, Gabriele Seleri, Andrea Ghedi, Umberto Ottonello, Flavio Falcinelli, Erminio Paniccia, Adriano Nardi, Alessandro Kosoveu, Angelo Brunero, Flaviano Gori, Claudio Re, Jader Monari, Enrico Macchia, Massimiliano Recchia, Matteo Bruna.

And lastly to foreign collaborators: Rick Warnett (Australia), Johan Bodin (Sweden), Klaus Betke (Germany), Väinö Lehtornata (Finland), David Isele (West Australia), Steve Olney (Australia), Manfred F. Kerckhoff (Germany), Dave Ewer (West Coast US, WA), Dave Oxnard (Holland), Trond Jacobsen (Halden, Norway) , William Ernest Payne (Dallas, GA, U.S), Peter Schmalkoke (Bonn, Germany), Hans Michlmayr (Western Australia), Harald Lutz (Sindelfingen, Germany), Clift Russell (Holbrook, Arizona) , Brian (Arizona, U.S.), Scott Fusare, Jean Marie Polard (France), John Meloy (Mariposa California in Sierra Nevada Mountain Foothills, U.S.), Tomislav Stimac (Zagreb, Croatia), Thierry Alves (Portugal), Kurt Diedrich (Germany), Dionysios Dimakos (Greece), Wolfgang Schippke (Germany), Jorgen Mortensen, (Denmark), Esko Kanerva (Finland), Eric Vogel (Sverige), C. Andersson (Sverige), Holger 'Geri' (Germany), Mike Aiello (U.S.), Costas Krallis (Greece).

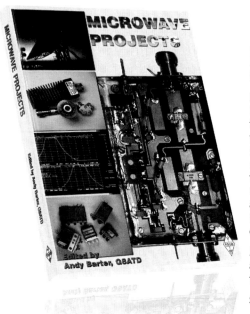

Microwave Projects

Edited by Andy Barter, G8ATD

Microwave Projects is aimed at those who are interested in build
ing equipment for the amateur radio microwave bands. Packe
full of ideas from around the world this book covers the subje
with a variety of projects. The book has many contributors wh
have a wealth of experience in this area and they have produce
many projects, design ideas, complete designs and modifica
tions of commercial equipment, for the book. This title provide
much useful information as to what can be achieved effective
and economically. Aimed at both the relative novice and the "o
hand" the book also covers useful theory of designing microwav
circuits and test equipment for the projects.

Microwave Projects is a must have book for all those who a
already active on the microwave bands and those looking for i
teresting projects to embark on.

Size 173x240mm, 200 pages, ISBN 9781-872309-90-2

Only £16.99

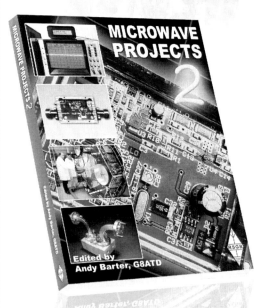

Microwave projects 2

By Andy Barter, G8ATD

Following the huge success of *Microwave Projects*, Andy Bart
G8ATD brings you more innovative projects from around the wor
If you are interested in building equipment for the amateur rac
microwave bands, the designs in this book are sure to please y
Projects have been selected from international authors and
of the projects use modern techniques and up to date comp
nents. Details of how to obtain ready-made boards are includ
with most projects.

If you are interested the microwave bands or just in amateur
dio construction *Microwave Projects 2* provides great ideas a
projects to satisfy everyone.

Size 240x175mm, 216 pages, ISBN 9781-905086-09-2

Only £16.99